Contents

Setting out 7

Introduction to Block 1 9

Part 1 Living in a connected world 11

1 Introduction 13

2 Understanding environment 14

 2.1 Where do you get your information from? 18

3 Connected world 22

 3.1 The story behind a graph 24

 3.2 A troubled paradise 31

 3.3 Monitoring biodiversity 37

4 The bare necessities 45

 4.1 Connected by the food we eat 46

 4.2 The environmental impact of food 48

 4.3 Food – necessity or choice? 51

 4.4 The journey so far 51

Summary of Part 1 53

Answers to SAQs 54

References 56

Part 2 Life in a changing world 57

1 Introduction 59

 1.1 Seeing the world *eco*-logically 59

 1.2 Imagining the world from space 64

2 Earth story: a walk through deep time 68

 2.1 Geological time 68

 2.2 Deep time 68

 2.3 Footsteps in the sand 70

    2.3.1 Days 1 and 2   71

    2.3.2 Days 3 and 4   72

    2.3.3 Day 5   74

  Summary of Section 2   80

3 Climate change and the carbon connection   **81**

  3.1 Climate, weather, global warming and global climate change   81

  3.2 The third planet   82

    3.2.1 The Earth's mean temperature   83

    3.2.2 The greenhouse effect   84

  3.3 The carbon connection   86

    3.3.1 The first carbon trail, the carbon cycle   86

    3.3.2 The second carbon trail, human influences   90

  3.4 Causes for concern   95

4 Sustainability: buzzword or byword?   **99**

Summary of Part 2   **104**

Answers to SAQs   **105**

References   **106**

Part 3 Treading lightly on the Earth   **107**

1 Introduction   **109**

  1.1 What is the carbon footprint and why is it important?   110

    1.1.1 Carbon dioxide and other greenhouse gases   110

    1.1.2 The carbon footprint boundary   111

  1.2 Individual and household carbon footprints   112

  Summary of Section 1   116

2 Not all footprints are equally heavy   **117**

  2.1 The carbon footprint of UK individuals and households   118

    2.1.1 The effects of imports and exports   118

    2.1.2 Including other greenhouse gases   118

U116

Environment: journeys through a changing world

Block 1
Setting out from home

Parts 1–4

Roger Blackmore, Maggie King, Robin Roy and Joe Smith

This publication forms part of the Open University course U116 *Environment: journeys through a changing world*. Details of this and other Open University courses can be obtained from the Student Registration and Enquiry Service, The Open University, PO Box 197, Milton Keynes MK7 6BJ, United Kingdom (tel. +44 (0)845 300 60 90; email general-enquiries@open.ac.uk).

Alternatively, you may visit the Open University website at www.open.ac.uk where you can learn more about the wide range of courses and packs offered at all levels by The Open University.

To purchase a selection of Open University course materials visit www.ouw.co.uk, or contact Open University Worldwide, Walton Hall, Milton Keynes MK7 6AA, United Kingdom for a brochure (tel. +44 (0)1908 858793; fax +44 (0)1908 858787; email ouw-customer-services@open.ac.uk).

The Open University
Walton Hall, Milton Keynes
MK7 6AA

First published 2009.

Copyright © 2009 The Open University

Edited and designed by The Open University.

Typeset by SR Nova Pvt. Ltd, Bangalore, India.

Printed and bound in the United Kingdom by Halstan Printing Group, Amersham.

ISBN 978 0 7492 2086 0

1.1

The paper used in this publication contains pulp sourced from forests independently certified to the Forest Stewardship Council (FSC) principles and criteria. Chain of custody certification allows the pulp from these forests to be tracked to the end use (see www.fsc-uk.org).

          2.1.3 The effect of people and places   120

          2.1.4 Identifying the carbon heavyweights   120

   2.2 International comparisons of carbon footprints   123

          2.2.1 Carbon footprints per person   123

          2.2.2 Total carbon footprints   124

          2.2.3 Differences between people and places   126

   Summary of Section 2   131

3 How heavy is your footprint?   **132**

   Summary of Section 3   134

4 Lightening your carbon load   **135**

   4.1 Carbon reduction targets   135

   4.2 Technical and behavioural actions   138

   Summary of Section 4   139

5 Treading lightly on the Earth   **140**

   5.1 Actions for lighter living   140

   5.2 Lighter living costs and constraints   145

   5.3 Moving towards a sustainable carbon footprint   146

   Summary of Section 5   155

6 Who's responsible for lightening carbon footprints?   **156**

   6.1 'I', 'we' or 'they'?   156

   6.2 The role of individuals and households   156

   6.3 The role of active citizens and communities   158

   6.4 The role of governments and business   160

   Summary of Section 6   161

Summary of Part 3   **162**

Answers to SAQs   **163**

References   **167**

Part 4 Building towards sustainability 169

1 Introduction 171

2 Coping with climate change: one wedge at a time 175

    2.1 Pacala and Socolow's wedges 175

    2.2 Critiques of the wedges approach: climate change = politics 184

3 Translating sustainability: the example of One Planet Living 189

4 Building sustainability 196

    4.1 Building Eden 196

    4.2 Pioneer builders 204

5 Building policies that face the future 208

Summary of Part 4 217

Answers to SAQs 218

References 220

Acknowledgements 221

Setting out

Why is this course called *Environment: journeys through a changing world*?

We are all living in a period of unparalleled change. In the first years of the twenty-first century the human population grew to well over 6 billion – up from just over 1.5 billion in 1900. In 2008 the urban population became larger than the rural population for the first time in human history.

Along with this came a startling growth in economic wealth and technological capacity. In 1900 the horseless carriage was a (dangerous) toy of the very wealthy. In 2007 the Indian car maker Tata produced the Nano – a four-door hatchback car that cut the price of the cheapest vehicle in the world by half (to around £1300), giving many millions of potential new drivers the freedoms of the private car. At the same time, communications technologies can now send new ideas and debates hurtling around the world instantly and cheaply.

However, this interconnected world of opportunities and pleasures has come with an unexpected price tag. Modern life may literally be costing the Earth, and time is running out. Economic development has raced ahead of human capacity to understand and limit the damage it can generate. Researchers have been working to understand both local and global environmental change, and humanity's role in these processes. Together with others, from politicians to architects, they have also been playing a part in finding solutions.

Studying this course will take you on a personal journey and provide you with some essential knowledge and skills that will help you to become more aware and informed of both the causes and the concerns of environmental change.

Studying the environment is becoming increasingly interdisciplinary. This is because those involved: scientists, policy makers, engineers, and many others, find that only by sharing the different approaches of their disciplines can they understand fully the complex global issues of today and so promote effective action. As you work through the course material you will encounter some of this variety of approaches. The course will guide you and help you appreciate how together these approaches contribute to a fuller understanding of environmental issues and debates.

The course will take you to some of the most fascinating parts of the planet that are important in terms of understanding environmental change. This tour of our interconnected world will visit six destinations.

Home

The first destination is about finding your bearings (and getting your bags packed). This is rather like reading a travel guide before you head off on a journey, and will introduce you to some of the language, ideas and context that you will need as you start to make more sense of environmental change. It will also get you to assess your own environmental impact in terms of your carbon footprint, and thinking about how to reduce it.

Arctic

You will be exploring a place that has long fascinated researchers, artists and adventurers. The Arctic is now thought of as a kind of early warning system in relation to climate change. You will be given a sense of the different ways in which environmental change is investigated and communicated, and experienced by the people who live there.

Nile

By contrast, your trip to the Nile will take in this very diverse region of tropical forest, desert, vital agricultural land and cities. This very diversity makes it an illuminating place to explore environmental conflicts (between nature conservation and community interests, and between different human interests) and some of the efforts to overcome them.

Amazon

Considered the richest storehouse of the world's biological diversity, this stop on the journey will not only help you to understand the environmental science of tropical forests but also connect your own daily choices to the fate of what has been called 'the Earth's lungs'. Scientists are mostly only visitors to the forests: you will also be in contact with members of indigenous communities that want to secure their future in their home.

China

The pace of economic, and hence environmental, change is perhaps greatest in the planet's most populous country. You will follow the migration of people from countryside to city, look at agricultural practices and gain insights into the difficult task of balancing wealth and new opportunities against protecting the world's environmental riches.

Cities

The last destination is the world's first truly global city – London. It was the hub of a global empire in the nineteenth century and brought millions of people into one place to make a future for themselves. It had to invent water, energy and transport systems to make a city healthy and workable. You will explore the ideas that aim to make the city economically, socially and environmentally more sustainable, contrasting what's happening in London with initiatives in China and elsewhere.

If you've already had a look at the U116 *Course Guide* you will see that the aims of the course are to:

- help you understand the current debates regarding environment and sustainability and enable you to participate from an informed position
- show how the planet undergoes processes of environmental change brought about by human activity and natural processes

- help you recognise and engage with strategies that might counter the adverse effects of human activity on our environment
- prepare you for further academic study by helping you to develop your study skills.

These aims have informed all the stops on the journey that has been planned for you. Achieving these will enable you to explore how and why different parts of the world are changing and how people, plants and animals are living within their changing environment. The course will show you how people are striving to understand, manage and protect our environment. It will help you to make sense of some of the stories and articles that you hear and read about in the media. By the end of the journey you will be able to do more than follow debates about environmental issues: you will be in a position to lead discussions with colleagues, family and friends, and to play an active part in addressing some of the great challenges of the day.

If you have not already done so, make sure that you look at the U116 Course Guide either now or at the end of Part 1.

1 Introduction to Block 1

Block 1, *Setting out from home,* is about helping you to find your bearings as you start the course journey. Part 1, *Living in a connected world,* introduces you to some of the language, ideas and contexts that you will need as you start to make more sense of environmental change. It also introduces key skills to help you become a more effective learner as you work your way through the course. A recurrent theme of Block 1 is the link between environmental change and the use of carbon by living things. Part 2, *Life in a changing world,* discusses the history of the Earth and the role of carbon in influencing the Earth's climate. Discussion of global warming and human influence leads to Part 3, *Treading lightly on the Earth,* where you investigate your individual and household environmental impact in the form of your carbon footprint, and explore options to reduce it. Part 4, *Building towards sustainability,* looks at the contribution that individuals and institutions can make in influencing sustainable building practices using specific examples, and discusses ways of moving to a sustainable built environment.

Part 1
Living in a connected world

Roger Blackmore and Maggie King

Introduction

Part 1, *Living in a connected world*, has two main aims.

The first, borrowing from the idea of setting out on a journey, is to equip you with some key ideas and skills that will help you appreciate and understand environmental change as you 'travel' through the course. It introduces the concept of environment and the complexity of environmental issues and problems. It also introduces key skills to help you read and understand both descriptive and numerical information presented in written form and in diagrams. Most of the activities in Part 1 focus on these skills.

The second aim is to provide examples of the connected world we live in, a taster of the journey to come, by taking a visit to Hawaii. Two topics are explored: changes to the composition of the atmosphere and changes to biological diversity. The ways in which this information is collected are discussed, and connections between human activity and what has been observed are explored. Part 1 ends with a discussion of modern lifestyles and an exploration of changing patterns of food consumption. It reminds us that we are living in a connected world and that our actions have global consequences.

2 Understanding environment

What do we mean when we use the term *'environment'*? What pictures does the word conjure up in your mind? Words may suggest different things to different people, particularly words that do not have a precise meaning. Figure 1.1 shows a compilation of images used by environmental organisations on their websites. They show a variety of images, and quite a few include people.

Dictionaries and encyclopedias provide several definitions and descriptions of the word 'environment', but most give a sense of the totality of everything that surrounds and influences *something*. In this course, we will use the word to refer to the surroundings and influences on *living things*, including humans. So, the concept of environment refers to all the conditions that surround and influence living things; for example, light, temperature, water and other living things.

The phrase 'the environment' is sometimes used to stand for 'the natural world', in contrast to the world of human society. However, the meaning of the term has moved away from one which assumes that humans are separate from nature, though surrounded by it, towards one which assumes that we are part of nature and that human society is dependent on physical and biological processes for its continued survival (even as it alters it). This is the view taken by this course.

The environment of any form of life is not just something passive and static: it also provides an active life-support system. Our environment is our life-support system, from which we draw food, water, and the air that we breathe and into which we discharge various wastes and other products. We therefore need not just to think of it as a collection of parts, but also to consider the interactions between the parts, and the forms of energy such as heat and light that drive these interactions. The reason why there is so much interest in 'the environment' today is that we are learning how much our behaviour affects our environment, which in turn is going to affect us. Many parts of our environment are now changing rapidly and our choices will decide the nature and magnitude of these changes.

(b) *Friends of the Earth*

(a) © *Still Pictures*

(e) © *Photodisc*

(c) © *Greenpeace/Olivares*

(d) © *Adam Oswell/WWF-Canon*

(g) *The Environment Trust*

(f) © *Edward Parker/WWF-Canon*

Figure 1.1 Images from environmental organisations

Figure 1.2 illustrates some recent headlines on environmental topics from newspapers and the Web. The messages put forward tend to range between two extremes: that either we are all doomed, or that there is not really a problem and the issue has been overstated. You may not agree with some of the sentiments, but since you have chosen to study this course it is likely that you have your own views on the topics shown in Figure 1.2. More generally, you may be concerned about particular environmental issues.

Activity 1.1   Environmental concerns

Spend a few minutes thinking about the following four questions. Write down a few of your thoughts before reading the discussion that follows.

* Make a list of three or four environmental issues that concern you now.
* Why are you concerned?
* Are you concerned mainly about the current state of affairs, or about what may happen in the future?
* What are the main influences on your views on environmental issues?

Discussion

The first point to emphasise is that there are no right or wrong answers to questions such as these. The issues that you identify as important will depend on your circumstances, your priorities and your values. For example, your main interest may be in global environmental issues; alternatively, you may be concerned about a particular local problem that directly affects you.

Here are a few issues you might have noted down: climate change; threats to rainforests and biodiversity and creatures such as whales or tigers; depletion of vital natural resources such as oil and gas; worries about ethical issues such as poverty, fair trade or treatment of animals. All these have a global dimension and there are many more. At the other end of the scale, if you live on a flood plain, concern about flooding of your local environment might be high on your list. Noise, air pollution, waste and litter, threats to individual creatures or plants, from newts to wild flowers may be on your list, as may be protection of open spaces, or access to them.

You may find that you are concerned personally and imagine that life will perhaps become more difficult and unpleasant for you in the medium- to long-term future for you and your family. You could also be concerned generally about the state of the planet and the loss of plants and animals and possible human hardships. Or you may just feel that there must be something to really worry about because of all the 'doom and gloom' about the environment that is always in the media.

It is quite possible that you are concerned about both current issues and the future. However, your attitude to the future can often be a measure of how optimistic or pessimistic you are – about environmental matters or generally. Optimists tend to believe things will get better, pessimists that they can only get worse. If you are more worried about the future than the present, you are likely to be pessimistic. However, your choice may be more influenced by your personal circumstances, your age, and whether you have children. If you have children it is natural to be concerned about their welfare and future, which is not the same as being pessimistic.

A whole range of people and factors are likely to influence your views: family members; friends; work colleagues; organisations; books and journals; TV news; newspapers; the Web. Note that this is very similar to asking the question 'Where do you get your information from?' which is discussed in the next section.

Figure 1.2 Collage of recent headlines on environmental topics

The previous activity highlights several points about environmental issues and how to respond to them. First, there are different dimensions to environmental issues ranging from the local to the global. Second, your viewpoint may depend upon your circumstances. If you are a subsistence farmer living on the poverty line, your main concern will be to protect your livelihood. Any environmental factors that cause illness, or affect your animals or crops – pests and diseases, and floods and drought – are likely to weigh more heavily than, say, noise *pollution* or concern for open spaces. Third, who you are and where you get your information from will probably influence you.

A further observation is that many environmental issues are complex. By this I mean that an issue may have many causes, and that different groups of people or interest groups may disagree on all aspects of the issue or how to solve it. For example, many people argue in favour of *renewable energy* as a contribution to preventing climate change, but people in affected areas often resent wind farms being placed near them, and other groups are concerned about the effect that wind farms may have on birds and bats. This means that environmental issues have social and political dimensions. Scientific and technical information is also needed to provide guidance to affected parties, but is unlikely to provide a 'right' answer of itself. To reach agreement between different groups means understanding and respecting other viewpoints; not always an easy task, but something you will encounter often as you work through this course.

Study note: using the Glossary

As explained in the *Course Guide*, technical terms or familiar words that are used in a particular way when writing about the environment are in bold when first used and are explained in the Glossary. You do not need to stop each time you come across one of these terms as this may interrupt your reading and understanding. You can look up the word later if necessary. However, if you are having difficulty understanding the passage because of a term that's in the Glossary, it may help to stop and refer to it.

2.1 Where do you get your information from?

In the previous section you were asked about your views on environmental issues and what influenced your views and opinions: the media, journals, friends, family, and other sources. So how do you know which information is reliable? Who can you trust to help you find out what is going on? Information is presented in very different ways, depending on the provider's intention. They may be trying to persuade the intended audience of a particular point of view, they may be misinformed, or it may simply be a good news story that will attract a large audience.

For instance, if the writer is from the nuclear industry, an article about a proposed new power station is likely to argue in favour of it, whereas many authors who are environmentalists, or someone living near the proposed site, might be very much against, unless they consider the new jobs that the project would bring to the area. So where does that leave the reader? Maybe none the wiser, but perhaps persuaded more to one viewpoint than the other.

The implication is that you have to be careful about assessing situations and forming opinions from information you receive from any source, and that involves always considering the origin and reliability of information.

The course team has tried to inform you as objectively as it can, with supporting evidence where appropriate, so that you can form *your own* opinions about our changing environment. But you need to recognise that, even so, the authors of U116 have their own particular biases and world views and these may well still colour what is presented.

Study note: reading actively

As you go through this course you will be introduced to some helpful study tips and hints on how to be an active and more effective learner.

Studying will inevitably require a considerable amount of reading, and this can at times seem a somewhat formidable task. However, there are techniques that you can employ to make it a more manageable task.

To get the most out of your reading it is helpful if you think about why you are reading. If you can decide before you start, and keep this purpose in mind as you read, you will find that you are more engaged and hence a more effective reader.

Activity 1.2   Different messages

Read the two polar bear articles below, written by different authors and taken from different publications.

As you read, consider the following questions:

- Where are the articles taken from?
- Are the two articles in agreement about the trend in polar bear numbers, or not?
- Are they written in the same style?
- What do you see as the intention of the two authors?

Polar bears in danger? Is this some kind of joke?

James Delingpole

The Times, 12 November 2007

Why don't polar bears eat penguins? Because their paws are too big to get the wrappers off, obviously. It's not a joke you hear so often these days, though, because polar bears are now a serious business. They're the standard-bearers of a tear-jerking propaganda campaign to persuade us all that, if we don't act soon on climate change, the only thing that will remain of our snowy-furred ursine chums will be the picture on a pack of Fox's glacier mints.

First there came the computer-generated polar bear in Al Gore's An Inconvenient Truth; then that heartrending photo, syndicated everywhere, of the bears apparently stranded on a melting ice floe; then the story of those four polar bears drowned by global warming (actually, they'd perished in a storm).

Now, in a new cinema release called Earth – a magnificent, feature-length nature documentary from the makers of the BBC's Planet Earth series – comes the most sob-inducing "evidence" of all: a poor male polar bear filmed starving to death as a result, the quaveringly emotional Patrick Stewart voiceover suggests, of global warming.

Never mind that what actually happens is that the bear stupidly has a go at a colony of walruses and ends up being gored to death.

The bear wouldn't have done it, the film argues, if he hadn't been so hungry and exhausted. And why was he hungry and exhausted? Because the polar ice caps are melting, thus shortening the polar bears' seal-hunting season.

Having been up to the bears' habitat in Svalbard, I do have a certain amount of sympathy with these concerns. To claim, however, that they are facing imminent doom is stretching the truth. In 1950, let us not forget, there were about 5,000 polar bears. Now there are 25,000.

No wonder Greenpeace had trouble getting polar bears placed on the endangered species list. A fivefold population increase isn't exactly a catastrophic decline.

But never let the facts get in the way of a good story. The doom-mongers certainly won't. Despite evidence from organisations such as the US National Biological Service that in most places polar bear populations are either stable or increasing, *Ursus maritimus* will continue to top the eco-hysterics' list of animals in danger because it's so fluffy and white and photogenic.

If you're really that worried about their demise, I'd book yourself a ticket to Churchill, Manitoba, where the evil buggers (about the only creature, incidentally, that actively preys on humans) are so rife they're almost vermin.

And if things get really bad, we can always ship the survivors off to Antarctica where, unlike the North Pole, the ice shelf appears to be growing. Then the joke would be even less comprehensible. Why don't polar bears eat penguins? But they do, actually!

Climate myths: Polar bear numbers are increasing

Phil McKenna

New Scientist, 16 May 2007

Polar bears have become the poster children of global warming. The bears spend most or all of the year living and hunting on sea ice, and the accelerating shrinking of this ice appears to pose a serious threat. The issue has even become politically sensitive.

Yet recently there have been claims that polar bear populations are increasing. So what's going on? There are thought to be between 20,000 and 25,000 polar bears in 19 population groups around the Arctic. While polar bear numbers are increasing in two of these populations, two others are definitely in decline. We don't really know how the rest of the populations are faring, so the truth is that no one can say for sure how overall numbers are changing.

The two populations that are increasing, both in north-eastern Canada, were severely reduced by hunting in the past and are recovering thanks to the protection they and their prey now enjoy.

The best-studied population, in Canada's western Hudson Bay, fell by 22% from 1194 animals in 1987 to 935 in 2004, according to the US Fish and Wildlife Service. A second group in the Beaufort Sea, off Alaska's north coast, is now experiencing the same pattern of reduced adult weights and cub survival as the Hudson Bay group.

A comprehensive review [1] by the US Fish and Wildlife Service concluded that shrinking sea ice is the primary cause for the decline seen in these populations, and it recently proposed listing polar bears as threatened [2] under the Endangered Species Act. The World Conservation Union projects the bears' numbers will drop by 30% by 2050 [3] due to continued loss of Arctic sea ice.

[1] http://alaska.fws.gov/fisheries/mmm/polarbear/pdf/Polar_Bear_%20Status_Assessment.pdf

[2] http://www.fws.gov/home/feature/2006/PolarbearFAQ.pdf

[3] http://pbsg.npolar.no/docs/PBSG14proc.pdf

Discussion

The first article is from *The Times*, which is considered a reasonably serious and informed 'broadsheet', and the second is from the *New Scientist* (a publication that reports the latest scientific and technological news) where you might also expect to find environmental issues treated responsibly.

The articles are making entirely different assertions regarding polar bear numbers. The *Times* article states that numbers are increasing and the *New Scientist* article suggests that some populations are increasing and some are decreasing.

I would describe the *Times* article as a trying-to-be-funny 'rant' with no evidence to support the claims (except for the US National Biological Service, which appears to be a news-gathering organisation). The author's style is to convince the casual reader by making fun of those he disagrees with, and may be more likely to attract readers. On the other hand, the *New Scientist* article seems to be written in a more straightforward style that presents the information available with supporting evidence (US Fish and Wildlife Service and World Conservation Union, both of which are authentic scientific organisations), and links to references are given.

The writer in The *Times* is saying that claims about the demise of the polar bear are exaggerated, but there is also an underlying message here that global warming is not happening. The *New Scientist* writer presents the information based on evidence regarding polar bear numbers.

This activity illustrates how opposing views on environmental matters may be presented in the media. We are constantly being subjected to conflicting messages, views and opinions and it can be difficult to know what to think. Readers are unlikely to check who the writers of each item are or the origin or reliability of information provided (also known as provenance). However, it is important to realise that some caution is required when trying to assess the environmental issues and forming your own opinions.

3   Connected world

This section explores two stories of environmental change: one about a set of observations that contribute to our understanding of climate change, the other about changes to biological diversity. Both of these topics are global issues that you may have identified in Activity 1.1. The two stories are located on Hawaii, the first stop on your journey.

Hawaii is a group of islands in the middle of the Pacific Ocean 4000 kilometres from North America, the nearest major landmass. This means it is far away from major sources of air pollution and is a good place to study the state of the Earth's atmosphere.

Box 1.1   The island chain of Hawaii

Hawaii, shown in Figure 1.3, is a remote group of volcanic islands in the middle of the Pacific Ocean stretching in an arc from north-west to south-east. The oldest islands are in the north-west, where millions of years of erosion have given rise to stunning cliffs and ridges, covered with tropical vegetation, such as the Na Pali coast on the island of Kauai, pictured in Figure 1.3(b). In the south-east, volcanic eruptions still occur regularly on Big Island, though fortunately they are not explosive but take the form of lava flows that continue to create new slopes. The remoteness of the islands means that many of its native plants and animals are endemics, that is, they exist only here and are not found anywhere else in the world. However, Hawaii has long been colonised by seafaring Polynesians, with European and American settlers arriving much later. Both have had major impacts on the islands and its native plants and animals.

(a)

(b)   (c)   (d)

Figure 1.3 Images from Hawaii: (a) map of the Hawaiian Islands; (b) Hanakapiai Beach on the Na Pali coast; (c) waterfall; (d) the Mauna Loa Observatory on Big Island

3.1 The story behind a graph

The first story takes us to the top of a mountain in Hawaii, where scientists monitor changes in the atmosphere.

Hawaii is the largest and youngest island in the group. Because it has the same name as the island chain, it is often known simply as Big Island. The name is quite appropriate, because the island rises directly from the deep ocean. It has twin volcanic peaks over 4000 metres high, but when measured from the ocean floor the mountains rise higher than Everest; they are among the biggest on the planet. High up on the slopes of one of these peaks, Mauna Loa ('Long Mountain' in Polynesian), is a set of observatories. The site was chosen because it is far from most sources of air pollution, and usually above the clouds. It is also some distance from the site of most modern volcanic eruptions lower down the slopes. Occasionally other parts of Big Island suffer from a form of pollution called 'vog'. Short for 'volcanic smog', it occurs during eruptions under certain atmospheric conditions. Most of the observatories here serve astronomy: they house telescopes that look beyond the clear atmosphere to detect faint signals from far-off stars and galaxies. One, shown in Figure 1.3(d), is not a telescope, and its concerns are closer to home. It simply measures the composition of the surrounding atmosphere, and has been doing so steadily for over 50 years.

In this section, we explore a simple diagram from this record of the atmosphere in the form of a graph. It has become so celebrated that it is often known as the *Keeling Curve*, after the scientist who started and maintained the measurements. What is so important about the Keeling Curve? It happens to be the longest continuous record in the world – over 50 years – of *carbon dioxide* levels in the atmosphere. Because it showed very clearly, within a few years, that there was a steady increase of carbon dioxide in the atmosphere, it was one of the first major signs of global environmental change.

Carbon dioxide is a naturally occurring gas that is present in the atmosphere in comparatively small amounts, but is essential for animals and plants and the maintenance of life. It is also a *greenhouse gas*, which means that it helps regulate the temperature of the planet. In the last few hundred years, human activities such as burning oil, gas and coal, and clearing forests, have released large amounts of carbon dioxide into the atmosphere. This extra carbon dioxide, recorded by the Keeling Curve, is a major cause of the additional warming of the whole planet, which we know as *global warming*. The causes and consequences of this are explored in more detail in Part 2.

Diagrams are used widely by the media and by experts because they are an effective way of summarising information and presenting it visually. However, they can be very easy to misinterpret, they may well contain errors, or even be presented in a way that deliberately misleads. All diagrams should be examined carefully, and graphs are just one form of diagram. The next study note shows a typical graph, explains how to read it, and discusses what a graph can and can't show. It is used as an example only, so although the data is real enough, the exercise is about graphs, not fish!

Charles Keeling

Study note: reading a graph

Graphs are diagrams that show the relationship between two different quantities. In graphs, the relationship is shown by a straight line or a curve of plotted points (which may or may not be shown). The graph here, Figure 1.4, shows the relationship between fish production and time; in other words how fish production varies over time.

As with all diagrams, graphs follow a set of conventions. These are highlighted in the example shown here. The two quantities being described, fish production and time, are represented by the vertical and horizontal axes respectively. Each axis should be labelled clearly to indicate what units are used, and have a marked scale. In this example, the vertical axis represents fish production; the scale ranges from zero to 120, and the units are million tonnes. The horizontal axis shows the year the data was collected, from 1950 to 2010. There are two lines: one showing the catch of wild fish, the other farmed fish. In this case, individual data points for each year are not shown.

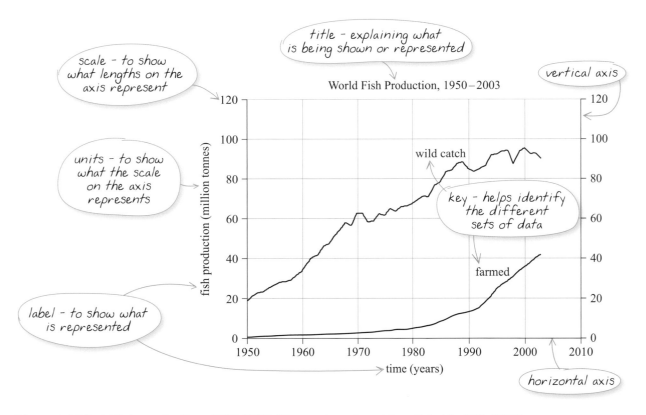

Figure 1.4 World fish production, 1950–2003 *(Source: based on data collated by EPI, 2005)*

What does the graph show?

1 Wild fish catch

From 1950 to 1970 there is a rise in the wild fish catch from 20 to 60 million tonnes. The catch continues to rise, but more slowly, between 1970 and 1995, from 60 to about 90 million tonnes. In the last few years, from 1995 to 2003, the catch remains within a certain range; it fluctuates between 90 and 95 million tonnes, but appears to be neither rising nor falling. Note that the curve is not smooth: there are small fluctuations from year to year, which give it a 'wobbly' look. Variability such as this is a feature of many graphs relating to the real world.

2 Farmed fish

Between 1950 and 1980, farmed fish output rises very slowly from almost zero to about 5 million tonnes. From 1980 to 2003 it rises more rapidly, particularly in the last ten years, from 1993, to just over 40 million tonnes.

What a graph doesn't show

Graphs only show what has happened, not the causes or reasons. In this example, the reasons for the rise in world fish production, even the fluctuations, cannot be found by looking at the lines. In addition, unless the curve represents a mathematical formula, you can't predict what happens next. Will the output of farmed fish continue to rise, will the wild fish catch stay the same, or rise, or fall? Any answers to such questions have to come from the accompanying text, which might discuss reasons or mechanisms for what is being shown.

To summarise, here are a few tips on what to look for in a graph, using the example in the study note.

- Is there a title or caption to the graph to explain what is being presented?

Yes, the title is World Fish Production, 1950–2003.

- If there is more than one line or curve, is there a key for each element?

Yes, the curves are labelled 'wild catch' and 'farmed'. In this case, the key is on the curves in the graph.

- Is there an explanation of the context, where and how the data was collected, and how representative it is?

Not here, because this graph has been taken from an article, but the article did explain the context, which was that the wild fish catch might have reached its limit.

- Are the relevant features or points of interest in the graph described or explained in the accompanying text?

The original text is not shown, but there is a description of the curves in the study note.

Figure 1.5 shows the Keeling Curve, the result of fifty years of measurements of the concentration of carbon dioxide in the atmosphere taken from Mauna Loa Observatory in Hawaii. Activity 1.3 examines this graph and curve in some detail through a series of questions and answers.

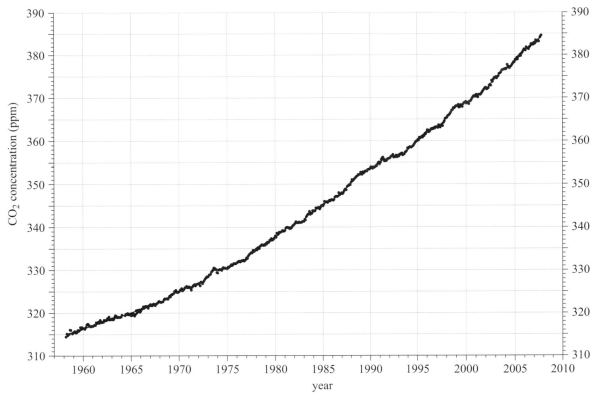

Figure 1.5 The Keeling Curve: 50 years of measurements from Mauna Loa of monthly average carbon dioxide concentration in the atmosphere, seasonally adjusted. Scripps CO_2 Program last updated October 2007 *(Source: Scripps, 2007a)*

Activity 1.3   The story behind a graph

(a) Look at the figure caption, then the labels and scales on the horizontal and vertical axes. Describe briefly what the graph represents.

Discussion

The caption states where the measurements were taken, who runs the programme, and what is measured: carbon dioxide concentration as a monthly average. This means that a point is plotted showing the average reading for each month, though the points are too close together to identify individual values. The horizontal axis indicates the year on a scale from 1957 to 2010 (the caption also mentions that the graph was last updated in October 2007). Note that the label simply says 'year', because in this

The term 'parts per million' describes the small fraction of carbon dioxide in the atmosphere in a manner that avoids using decimal points

case it is clear that the horizontal scale measures time. The vertical axis measures the concentration of carbon dioxide as parts per million (ppm) of air, and the scale runs from 310 ppm to 390 ppm.

(b) Describe what the curve on the graph shows.

Discussion

Between late 1957, when measurements started, and October 2007, the concentration of carbon dioxide in the atmosphere rose from about 315 ppm to approximately 385 ppm (reading the values from the graph). The rise is very steady throughout this period, but the slope becomes steeper in later years, indicating that the *rate* of rise has increased.

(c) By how much has the carbon dioxide concentration increased over 50 years? Has it increased ten times, twice, or by a fifth?

Discussion

Just by looking at the curve, you might be tempted to say that carbon dioxide concentration has increased by about ten times. This would be true if the vertical scale started at *zero*, but as discussed in (a) it ranges from 310 ppm to 390 ppm, so it is always important to check the range of each scale on the graph. Over 50 years, the curve rises from a starting value of 315 ppm to finish at about 385 ppm. It increases by 70 ppm (385 − 315) during this time, which is just over a fifth of the starting value. It is easy to get a false impression about the amount of change shown on a graph unless you check the scales.

(d) What will happen to the carbon dioxide concentration over the next 50 years?

Discussion

From the graph, it looks as though the concentration will continue to rise, but without knowing the causes of the increase it is not possible to make a safe prediction. The causes are discussed in Part 2 of this block.

(e) The graph shows that the concentration of carbon dioxide in the atmosphere over this period has been rising very steadily at the Mauna Loa site, possibly at an increasing rate. What doesn't it show?

Discussion

It doesn't tell you anything about global warming, or what or who has caused the increase in carbon dioxide in the atmosphere, only that it has been increasing. Nor does it tell you whether the same rise is seen elsewhere on the planet, how reliable the data is, or what will happen in the future.

(f) What further questions could be asked?

Discussion

Three further questions are prompted by the earlier discussions:

Question: Why does the vertical scale start at 310 ppm and not zero?

Discussion: The reason for starting the scale at 310 ppm instead of zero is to emphasise the element of interest, which is the increase in concentration, not the absolute level. The rise would be less clear if the scale ranged from zero to 400 ppm. There is no intention to deceive or mislead about the rate of change here, but you should always check the range shown on the graph to make sure exaggerated claims aren't being made.

Question: How representative is the data for the planet?

Discussion: When Keeling first started taking measurements of carbon dioxide concentrations, he spent time and effort to be sure on two points. First, that measurements taken from a site represented the air flowing past it and weren't influenced by local sources. This was a major reason for selecting the Mauna Loa Observatory, near the top of a mountain in the Pacific Ocean. Second, measurements were taken simultaneously from other parts of the planet, including from Antarctica. Comparisons showed that measurements of carbon dioxide concentration made in different parts of the globe differ by only one or two parts per million, so the Mauna Loa figures are representative of the global atmosphere.

Question: What does the caption mean by 'seasonally adjusted'?

Discussion: Figure 1.6 is the unadjusted graph showing the annual fluctuations. This shows the more detailed picture of variation within each year. Keeling discovered this annual variation, and reported it in a paper in

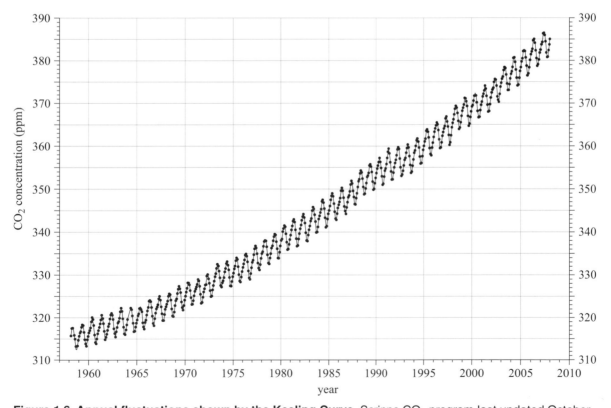

Figure 1.6 Annual fluctuations shown by the Keeling Curve. Scripps CO_2 program last updated October 2007 *(Source: Scripps, 2007b)*

the science journal *Tellus* in 1960. It shows that peak levels of carbon dioxide are reached in spring in the northern hemisphere, before plants on the northern landmasses and continental shelves start growing strongly again and absorbing carbon dioxide. The effect is far less prominent in the southern hemisphere, where there is less land. These fluctuations, though of interest to scientists, are often not the main point of showing the graph, so they are smoothed out. Figures 1.5 and 1.6 show the same phenomenon but are presented differently to give different emphasis. You will see both versions presented in textbooks and the media. The annual peak in the fluctuation each spring is an opportunity for a media headline, as this example illustrates: 'World carbon dioxide levels highest for 650,000 years, says US report', referring to the Mauna Loa Observatory (Adam, 2008). That was true, but hardly news: carbon dioxide levels have reached a new peak every spring for the last fifty years. What is more important is the underlying trend.

Finally, a few words of caution on interpreting data. Figure 1.7 reproduces the original observation points taken from the Mauna Loa Observatory in its early days, in 1958 and 1959. Look first at the measurements from 1958 only, marked in Figure 1.7 as Section A. At this stage you might conclude that the concentration of carbon dioxide was falling. It *was* falling, but it would be wrong to assume that it would keep on falling. In the following seven months, Section B, the concentration of carbon dioxide rose strongly.

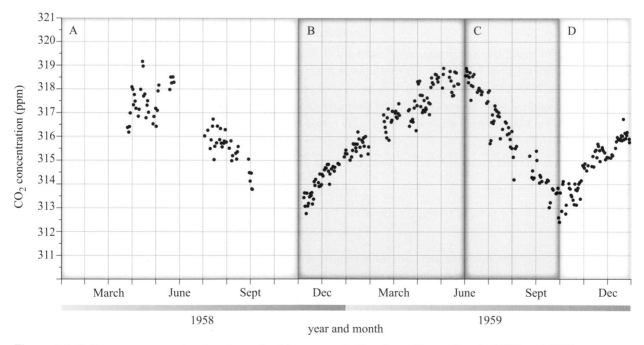

Figure 1.7 Daily measurements of carbon dioxide concentration from Mauna Loa in 1958 and 1959
(*Source: Keeling R., 2007*)

The pattern of seasonal variation emerges clearly only after the full two years of measurements, Sections A–D, are viewed side by side. This pattern (confirmed by similar fluctuations from other sites) is what led Keeling to report in his 1960 paper:

> A clearly defined seasonal trend is found at all locations in the northern hemisphere.

> *(Keeling C.D., 1960)*

It is clear that if you wanted to mislead, you could select a six-month sequence from this data to create a false conclusion. You could choose Section A to argue that concentration of carbon dioxide was falling, or Section B that it was rising very rapidly. Neither would be representative of any long-term trend, which is not apparent in Figure 1.7. This illustrates a general point about using data, which is to make sure that there are enough measurements, or that the measurements have been taken over a long enough time period to support the claims being made. It is also important to ensure that if a sample of data is used, it is representative of the whole set and hasn't been selected to show a trend or quantity which is not typical.

In fact, Keeling used more information than we have shown here before reporting his findings. He was able to compare measurements taken from several sites all over the world to ensure that what he observed in Mauna Loa was not just a local phenomenon. He also used other measurements taken directly above sites of growing vegetation in the northern hemisphere to propose an explanation for what was observed.

> These data, therefore, indicate that the seasonal trend in concentration observed in the northern hemisphere is the result of the activity of land plants.

> *(Keeling C.D., 1960)*

Although there is no sign of an underlying trend in Figure 1.7, Keeling noted a consistent rise of carbon dioxide concentration in the measurements taken from the southern hemisphere, which were not masked by seasonal fluctuations. Both findings were considered 'tentative' because they were based on relatively few measurements and over a short time span. They were confirmed only after a longer series of measurements were made and the trends persisted. The Keeling Curve is important because it shows that these trends have continued now for fifty years. Keeling had to fight several times to maintain the observations at Mauna Loa because taking comparatively straightforward measurements no longer seemed to be 'cutting edge' science. However, his persistence has proved to be his legacy, and the Keeling Curve demonstrates the importance of monitoring our planetary environment.

3.2 A troubled paradise

Hawaii has often been chosen in films as a location to represent either paradise or a primeval jungle. But are its forests quite what they seem? The second story is of a tropical forest that looks lush and untouched to the untrained eye, even though it has a walking trail through its heart. Here, you will explore human impact on *biodiversity*, a word derived from biological diversity. Put simply, it is a measure of how many types of organisms (living things) there are in a given place. You move to Oahu, one of the older islands in the chain, where Professor Richard Fortey, a senior *palaeontologist* at the Natural History Museum in London, writes of his experience of walking along a forest trail in his book *The Earth: An Intimate History* (Fortey, 2005[2004]). Although his book is mainly about geology, here he ponders the influence of geology and isolation on life and its diversity.

> The Hawaiian Islands were once pristine. As remote from any major continent as anywhere in the world, they were originally colonised by a mere handful of hardy, far-travelled plants and animals – birds, insects, reptiles – that subsequently evolved prolifically in their new Eden. The species that appeared as a consequence were endemics; that is they were found nowhere else in the world.

(Fortey, 2005 [2004], p. 39)

Oahu is now home to the only city on the island chain, Honolulu. Its name means 'sheltered bay', and nearby is Pearl Harbour. Today, in spite of the romantic name, Honolulu is full of traffic and busy shopping malls like many a US or UK city. However, you do not have to venture far outside the modern city borders before you encounter spectacular scenery. Figure 1.8 shows some examples.

Figure 1.8 Photos of tropical vegetation on the Manoa Falls trail, Hawaii: (a) vines; (b) yellow hibiscus; (c) waterfall

Although Fortey is a scientist, here he is appealing to your imagination to make his points about biodiversity.

> Not far behind Honolulu, mountains rise surprisingly quickly, and they are clothed in forest. There is an easy walk through it to the Manoa Falls north of Waikiki. The little path dodges this way and that through the trees, ever upwards, often muddy. This is more like the paradise of the movies: vast trees soar away above you, and their huge trunks are decked with climbing plants, some of them with enormous leaves, or heart-shaped foliage blotched with yellow patches. These vines seem vaguely familiar from florist's shops, though here they grow on a giant scale. There is an intense and humid odour of prolific growth. You can almost hear the shoots squeezing upwards towards the sun. There are pale yellow spikes of fragrant ginger flowers on either side of the path. […] Piping noises echo somewhere in the canopy way above. Half-seen birds such as these are obligatory in Eden. When the waterfall is reached […] a fickle spray that has plunged 200 feet down a lava flow. Bathing in a pool in the midst of a primeval jungle is the dream of paradise on the holiday brochure.
>
> But this, too, is a bogus paradise. Almost none of the plants that climb up the massive trees along the path are a native of O'ahu or the Hawaiian islands. Indeed, neither are the trees themselves. They are interlopers, brought to this remote place by humans. These plants settled in the tropics and thrived, displacing much of the native vegetation. The resemblance of the climbers decking the trees to pot plants is no coincidence: some of them are the same species that can be bought in a supermarket in Norfolk […] as commonplace in their way as tomato ketchup. Even the sweet-smelling ginger plant that looks so at home by the pathside […] is an aggressive coloniser. This place is not so much Paradise Lost as Paradise Replaced – a paradise of aliens dressed up to look as if they belong. The massive assurance of the trees is play acting.

(Fortey, 2005 [2004], p. 38)

Study note: reading with a purpose

As has already been mentioned in Section 2, one of the most basic and important skills of being a successful student is the ability to read actively and purposefully.

Focusing is a method of reading where you are concentrating on getting an overview of the text and trying to determine the main message. When confronted with a piece of reading you may find it helpful to glance through the material first so that you get the overall gist of what the piece is about, and maybe some hints of the important ideas. It can be helpful to look at the first and last sentences of each paragraph or, more generally, the first and final summarising paragraphs or sentences of the section or passage. Then, when you have some kind of an overview, you can reread the passage and highlight the essential points.

After reading a passage or section, it can be helpful to ask yourself whether you have understood the main points, so maybe a quick glance back over the material could answer this for you. You can then summarise your thoughts by making some notes of the main points. (Methods of note taking are discussed at a later stage, but for now use any that you are comfortable with.)

SAQ 1.1   Identifying the main point of a passage

Read again the passage above by Richard Fortey, then describe briefly his main point or message (Hint: The purpose of reading in this instance is to pick out from amongst the poetic language and details the main point that the author is trying to make. Try using the focusing technique mentioned in the study note.)

The hidden hand behind this landscape is human, not just in this forested valley but across the whole island chain. The first human settlers were Polynesian, expert sailors originally from South-East Asia and Indonesia, who colonised most of the islands of the Pacific Ocean. The first of many settlers probably reached Hawaii nearly two thousand years ago. Over time, they brought to the islands up to thirty new types of plants and crops including coconuts, banana, taro (a root crop) and sugar cane, as well as goats, pigs and dogs. Uninvited travellers such as black rats came too. The Polynesians introduced agriculture to the low-lying land, irrigation channels and terraces to some valleys and hunted the flightless birds. Some of the animals they brought along escaped into the surrounding forests.

The second wave of settlement began much later, in 1788, soon after the English explorer Captain Cook chanced upon the islands and encountered a culturally rich Polynesian kingdom. Though the first meeting between Europeans and Hawaiians was peaceful, this was the first contact between a culture based mostly on self-sufficiency and one based on capitalism, i.e. one that uses resources as commodities to buy and sell, not just to supply needs. Within a few years, Americans began logging forested slopes for sandalwood, a scented hardwood valued highly by the Chinese, and sold to them in exchange for tea. They introduced sugar plantations in the 1850s, and twenty years later cane fields were widespread. Both local people and immigrants were used to tend and harvest this crop; its demand for labour largely accounts for the diverse nature of the current population. Other cash crops followed, particularly pineapples and coffee. Although agriculture declined in the twentieth century, even in the 1970s one of the smaller islands, Lanai, was almost entirely given over to pineapple cultivation and was known as Pineapple Island. Today, tourism is now the main source of income for the island, but agriculture is still important. Sugar, pineapples, 'Kona' coffee and macadamia nuts are still significant exports, although now nurseries selling tropical plants and seedlings, and flowers such as orchids, are a bigger source of income.

Both waves of settlement have had major impacts on Hawaii's landscape and its biodiversity, but the biggest changes have occurred in the last 200 years. Hawaii is now part of the United States of America: it became the fiftieth state in 1959. It is tiny compared to the continental mainland, with only two-thousandths of the total land area, but it accounts for 70% of all recorded extinctions of species in the USA and three-quarters (75%) of all plants and animals listed as endangered in the USA. In this respect, Hawaii is typical of many other islands. Globally, since about 1500, most extinctions of species have taken place on oceanic islands like those of the Hawaiian chain.

A percentage, indicated by the % sign, simply means 'parts out of one hundred'. Thus 70% means seventy out of one hundred

Study note: handling new information

The remainder of Section 3 discusses threats to biodiversity, first on the Hawaiian Islands, then globally. You will be reading a fair amount of detailed information that is intended to help you make sense of some of the ideas being discussed. There may also be a number of terms from biology and ecology that are unfamiliar. You do not need to memorise them all, but you should become familiar with them as they are terms commonly used in the study of environment. Some of these terms are gathered together and explained in Boxes 1.2 and 1.3.

Box 1.2   Short descriptions of common terms from ecology and biology

Biosphere. The relatively thin layer around the Earth that supports life, including all ecosystems and organisms, on land, in the atmosphere and the oceans.

Biodiversity. The variety of life on the planet. The total diversity of all organisms and ecosystems.

Extinct. A species, or group of species, is extinct when the last individual has died.

Organism. Any living thing or being.

Species. A group of organisms whose members share similar characteristics and can interbreed and produce viable offspring.

Ecology. The study of the relationship of organisms with each other and with their environment. Ecologists use a variety of ways of looking at these relationships. Habitats and ecosystems are two examples.

Habitat. The physical and biological environment in which an organism lives. It is useful for describing *where* certain animals and plants live, and *who* they live with. The focus is usually on a particular organism. For example, bluebells are found in certain woodland habitats.

Ecosystem. A way of categorising parts of the biosphere that stresses the relationships and interdependence between organisms and their physical environment, and *how* these relationships function. For example, a small pond can be regarded as an ecosystem, whose healthy functioning can be affected by pollution, or the introduction of an invasive weed. A colony of bacteria in a drop of water can be regarded as an ecosystem at one end of a spatial scale, to the complete biosphere at the other.

Why have island species been so vulnerable? According to the International Union for the Conservation of Nature (**IUCN**, see Section 3.3), the two main causes of loss of biodiversity globally are the loss of habitat or its degradation and fragmentation, and the introduction of new, or 'alien', species to an area. These changes are nearly always a result of human activity, whether intended or not.

Life on remote islands is vulnerable for several reasons. Islands are often hilly or mountainous and can support a wide range of different habitats, but many may be of limited extent and they may support quite small populations. Many species of life on oceanic islands are found only on a particular island or island chain. In addition, most island populations have developed in the absence of land mammals, which find it difficult to cross large stretches of water. Flightless birds, and birds that build their nests on the ground, are easy prey for introduced mammals like rats and cats. Without pressure from grazing mammals, many island plants have developed no defences such as thorns or poisons that would deter grazing.

Since human occupation, Hawaii has lost 40% of its seventy bird species, and of those that remain three-quarters are threatened. Similarly, it has lost nearly three-quarters of more than a thousand species of land snail. The main culprit has probably been the black rat, which eats snails, insects, birds' eggs and nestling birds, as well as stripping branches from bushes. Goats have destroyed entire populations of native plants that have no resistance to grazing, and goats and wild pigs cause extensive damage to habitats such as rainforests and mountain bogs by eating plants and churning the ground.

> Nearly 200 of the 1500 native plant species in Hawaii are at risk of going extinct in the near future because they have been reduced to such low numbers. Approximately 90 percent of Hawaii's plants are found nowhere else in the world but they are threatened by alien invasive species such as feral goats, pigs, rodents and non native plants.
>
> *(IUCN, 2007d)*

SAQ 1.2   Actions affecting biodiversity

The first two paragraphs after SAQ 1.1 describe examples of actions by human settlers that have had an impact on the native biodiversity of Hawaii. Read through these two paragraphs again and identify, where possible, which actions come under the heading of (a) the introduction of new species, and (b) habitat loss and degradation.

Not all the actions described in the two paragraphs can be placed simply in these two categories; sometimes the two are interlinked. Thus invasive species may act by changing or destroying habitats, which is one of the points made about the 'bogus' paradise by Richard Fortey. There are also other threats to biodiversity, including:

- overexploitation of resources by hunting, fishing or extraction
- the effects of pollution and disease and, more recently,
- climate change.

The hunting of flightless birds by the first Hawaiians and logging by early Americans might come under the heading of overexploitation, but what of tourism? The effects of tourism are less easy to assign to a single factor because they are likely to have multiple impacts on many aspects of Hawaii's environment.

Finally, it is worth noting that although most of the changes discussed can be traced ultimately to human actions, they are very often not intended. It is highly unlikely that sailors welcomed the presence of rats aboard their ships, nor wished them to spread out and predate the local bird populations, effectively competing for high-quality food. Often, human intentions do not work out as expected because the consequences are not understood. Ecological systems (ecosystems) rely on a complex web of interactions: upsetting one component is likely to alter others, and often in ways that are not anticipated. An example is the introduction of the mongoose onto sugar plantations to control rats. It was not successful because rats are most active at night-time, while mongooses hunt during the day. The mongooses were thus not effective in controlling rats; they turned instead to easier sources of food, such as birds' eggs and young birds. Thus an animal introduced to control one invasive species became another. The mongoose became established on all the main islands in Hawaii apart from one. The exception was Kauai, which is the only island now supporting significant populations of ground-nesting birds.

3.3 Monitoring biodiversity

Native species and habitats on remote islands like Hawaii have been in retreat in recent centuries. Remote islands are known to be affected particularly badly, and some of the reasons why this is happening on Hawaii have been discussed. But what is known of the state of biodiversity across the planet? Who is monitoring what is happening?

A particular challenge for biologists and ecologists is how to record and monitor the state of biodiversity, because the idea encompasses the total variety of life on the planet. Recall the description of biodiversity in Box 1.2 that says it is 'the total diversity of all organisms and ecosystems at a variety of spatial scales'. One way of measuring the current state of biodiversity is to count the number of species threatened by extinction. This focus on the diversity of organisms is for practical reasons: most species are quite distinctive and it is possible to count and monitor them. Box 1.3 describes how organisms are classified.

Box 1.3   Classification of living organisms

The classification of living organisms has been a fundamental part of biological study for centuries. The science of classification is called *taxonomy*. Modern classification systems are based primarily on groupings of organisms that have shared physical characteristics, but also take account of evolutionary relationships between different groups. Many of these groupings are very familiar; for example, if it has feathers then we know it's a bird. Within the 'bird' group there are other groups such as eagles, sparrows and parrots. And, at a higher level, birds can be grouped with mammals, reptiles and amphibians because they all have backbones (they are vertebrates) and are, of course, all animals. These different levels of grouping can be extended into a hierarchy of classification from *kingdoms*, such as animals, at the top, down to species at the bottom.

A complete hierarchy is shown schematically in Figure 1.9.

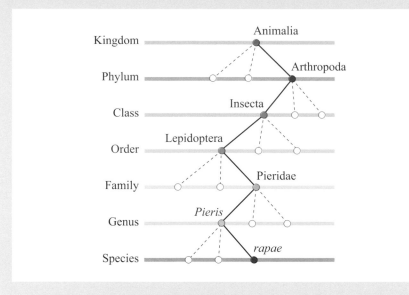

Figure 1.9 A hierarchy of classification

There are intermediate stages and subdivisions between these main levels as well. It's not usual for an organism to be described using all the classification levels, but any organism can be precisely defined in this way. For example, the Small White butterfly, found in Europe, whose caterpillars feed on the cabbage family, can be described thus:

Kingdom: Animalia (all animals)

Phylum: Arthropoda (all animals with jointed appendages)

Class: Insecta (the majority of arthropods with six legs)

Order: Lepidoptera (all butterflies and moths)

Family: Pieridae (butterflies including the cabbage whites and others)

Genus: *Pieris* (includes Small White, Large White, Green-veined White)

Species: *rapae* (Small White butterfly).

Each level of the hierarchy defines and describes the characteristics in a more and more precise way, down to the exact species. The usual way to refer to most organisms is simply to use genus and species, so in this case it's *Pieris rapae*.

The use of Latin is standard practice in taxonomy; for example Animalia rather than animals, Insecta rather than insects. It provides an internationally accepted and universal convention for describing living organisms. The butterfly known as the Small White butterfly and Small Cabbage White butterfly in Britain is known as the white cabbage worm in the US and i farfalla di bianco di cavolo in Italy. Using the name *Pieris rapae* when referring to the same butterfly avoids confusion wherever you are in the world.

Notice that I described Figure 1.9 as 'a' hierarchy rather than 'the' hierarchy. Rather surprisingly perhaps, given that this has been the subject of study for centuries, there is no common agreement amongst taxonomists on the detail of the hierarchy. Some systems have five kingdoms, which are:

Animalia

Plantae

Fungi

Protista or Protoctista

Bacteria.

This is the system referred to in Part 2 of this block. Other systems divide the bacteria into two groups, making six kingdoms. More recent systems have a higher rank above kingdom, called domain, in which the kingdoms are grouped into three domains. Also note the alternative names of Protista and Protoctista. This kingdom consists mostly of single-celled microscopic organisms, but slightly different groupings, and therefore different names, are used by different authorities. There are further variations as well, but they are too numerous to explore here.

Perhaps it shouldn't be a surprise that taxonomy is such a complex and debated subject when you consider how many living things there are. Estimates of how many species exist vary widely, from 5 million to 100 million, but most have yet to be identified. Somewhere between 1.8 and 2 million species have been identified and described, and more are discovered all the time.

Evolution was mentioned in the opening paragraph of this box, and it is the processes of evolution that have led to this great variety.

Studying living organisms, including those only found in the fossil record, and classifying them according to their similarities and differences, helps reveal how evolutionary pressures have gradually, over millions of years, led to diversification and separation into millions of different species.

The idea of a hierarchy for the classification of organisms, from kingdoms or domains to species, helps provide a perspective on the use of species as an indicator of the state of biodiversity. Taking the example in Box 1.3, the order Lepidoptera (butterflies and moths) represents the diversity of all its individual species. The loss of an order, all butterflies and moths for example, would be of more significance to total biodiversity than the loss of a single species belonging to it. In addition to the direct loss of all the species in the order, the removal of this unique group would have a major impact on the stability of the many habitats and ecosystems in which they play a key role, both as pollinators of plants and as a source of food for other animals. However, the following discussion refers only to species and kingdoms; other taxonomic groups in the hierarchy are usually referred to as 'groupings of species'.

One authoritative source of information on threatened species is the International Union for the Conservation for Nature, or World Conservation Union, usually known by the initials IUCN. The IUCN was founded in 1948 and brings together 78 states, more than a hundred government agencies, 800 *non-governmental organisations (NGOs)* and thousands of scientists. Each year the IUCN produces a *Red List of Threatened Species* and its website describes how many species are threatened with extinction.

Phrases such as 'threats to biodiversity' and 'endangered species' are used commonly by the media when discussing environmental problems. They are also used by NGOs campaigning to protect certain species. These phrases refer to categories defined by the IUCN. The 'threatened' category means a species or group of species threatened with extinction. Within this category, other terms are used to describe the level of risk. Those most at risk of imminent extinction are 'critically endangered' (some are flagged as possibly extinct), followed in order of decreasing risk by 'endangered', then 'vulnerable'. Each term is described by strict criteria based on a combination of biological factors such as rate of decline, population size and distribution, and area of geographic distribution or range (IUCN, 2007a).

The IUCN also provides fact sheets on individual species, describing their conservation status and distribution, and the main threats to their survival. For example, in 2007 it provided fact sheets and pictures of nine key species it chose to highlight. Figure 1.10 shows these species (IUCN, 2007b).

Figure 1.10 Threatened species featured in the IUCN Red List, 2007, with current threat status: (a) White-headed vulture (vulnerable); (b) Banggai cardinal fish (endangered); (c) Gharial (critically endangered); (d) Bornean orang-utan (endangered);); (e) Western lowland gorilla (critically endangered); (f) Mauritius echo parakeet (endangered); (g) Sumatran orang-utan (critically endangered (h) Baiji or Yangtse River Dolphin (critically endangered, possibly extinct); (i) Galapagos corals (critically endangered; some species possibly extinct) *(Source: IUCN, 2007b)*

SAQ 1.3   Threatened species

(a) How many of the species shown in Figure 1.10 belong to the kingdom Animalia?

(b) Which of the species shown in Figure 1.10 are least at risk of extinction, according to the IUCN?

How representative of total diversity are the Red List assessments? One way to answer this question is to compare the number of species identified for each kingdom with those assessed for the IUCN. In Figure 1.11, each of the five kingdoms is represented by a circle whose area is in proportion to the number of known species. Note that a sub-grouping of the animal kingdom, the vertebrates, is also shown. The lower half of Figure 1.11 shows the number of species assessed by the IUCN, also grouped by kingdoms.

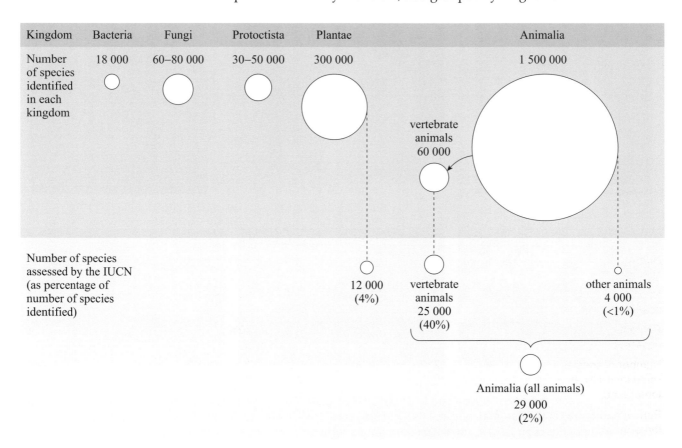

Figure 1.11 Numbers of identified species assessed by the IUCN, categorised by kingdom *(Sources: Natural History Museum, 2008; IUCN, 2007c)*

SAQ 1.4   Identified and assessed species

(a) Which kingdom has the most number of identified species?

(b) According to Figure 1.11, how many species have been assessed by the IUCN?

(c) Approximately what proportion of the two million species identified has been assessed by the IUCN?

Figure 1.11 shows that the IUCN has made assessments of only a very small proportion of the known species from the plant and animal kingdoms. Two-thirds of all assessments have been from the kingdom with the largest number of identified species, the animal kingdom. However, the figure also shows that IUCN assessments have concentrated on one grouping within the animal kingdom, the vertebrate animals: mammals, birds, amphibians, reptiles and fish. The much larger number of other animals, which includes insects, worms, molluscs, starfish and jellyfish, etc., is less well represented.

Table 1.1 gives a breakdown of the total number of identified species of vertebrate animals in the world, and the numbers assessed by the IUCN. Numbers are given for mammals, birds, amphibians, reptiles and fish. The self-assessment questions that follow check your understanding of the figures in the table.

Table 1.1 Vertebrate animals: total number of species described in each group and the number assessed by the IUCN Red List

	Vertebrate animal				
	Mammals	**Birds**	**Amphibians**	**Reptiles**	**Fish**
Number of identified species	5416	9960	6199	8240	30 000
Number of species assessed by IUCN	4863	9960	5915	1380	3119
Percentage of species assessed	90%	100%	95%	17%	10%
Number of species listed by IUCN as threatened	1094	1217	1808	(235)	(320)*
Percentage of species threatened	22%	12%	31%	(30%)	(25%)

Source: based on data from IUCN, 2007c.

*The numbers in brackets are estimates based on an incomplete sample only.

SAQ 1.5   Making sense of data

(a) Which grouping of vertebrate animals has the largest number of identified species?

(b) Which grouping has the largest number of species assessed by the IUCN?

(c) Which grouping has the highest percentage of species assessed?

(d) Which grouping has the highest number of species threatened?

The IUCN Red List represents the best information we have on the state of species and groupings of species. At the moment, this information covers only a small selection of known species (which is itself only a small sample of the expected total). The current selection has a bias towards certain groupings of familiar animals, such as birds, mammals and amphibians. The emphasis in reports on these groupings is perhaps inevitable because the information on them is more complete. All other species, including those from other kingdoms which are often less visible or less well known, are likely to be just as significant, but we won't know their status until they too are identified and assessed.

Nevertheless, the figures from the IUCN, such as those in Table 1.1, now suggest that between ten and thirty per cent of species currently assessed are in danger of extinction. Is this figure higher than would be expected from studying extinction rates in the past? Comparing the rate of known extinctions over the last 100 years with past rates estimated from the fossil record suggests that the current rate is between 50 and 500 times greater (Millennium Ecosystem Assessment, 2005). It seems likely that, apart from exceptional periods in the Earth's history when *mass extinctions* occurred, a topic taken up in Part 2, the current threat to biodiversity is highly unusual.

As was the case with Hawaii, the causes of most recent extinctions and current threats to species can probably be traced to human action. According to the IUCN, '99% of threatened species are at risk from human activities' (IUCN, 2006). Section 4 explores some of the reasons why the way modern societies live is having such far-reaching effects.

The bare necessities

4

Why are modern societies and economies having such an impact on our environment? We start by asking what are the necessities of modern life. One way to approach this question is to ask what aid workers need to bring to a disaster area once people are out of immediate danger.

Activity 1.4   Emergency relief

Make a list of the items that would be essential to maintain life after a disaster.

Discussion
Most lists would include food, clean water for drinking and washing, shelter or temporary accommodation, warm clothing, fuel for cooking, sanitation and medical care. The list is likely to be similar wherever the disaster occurs, whether in England or Africa, although the materials provided would be adapted to suit the conditions after the disaster, and climate and culture. Today we would expect to provide the best medical care available and to evacuate the injured to hospital, though you could argue that this goes beyond the bare necessities. Security is also a necessity, although it is not usually the responsibility of aid workers.

This is what is needed for *temporary* relief, but the hope would be that those who suffered would be able to return as soon as possible to their homes, their livelihoods and their previous way of life.

Living on the basic necessities alone means living in poverty, and this is the prevailing condition for many people throughout the world. Most in such a situation aspire to a better life for themselves and their families. In any modern society, the great majority of the population would expect and strive for better living conditions than this.

For example, a major study asked a large number of people about the minimum income required to live an acceptable social life in Britain in the early twenty-first century. Among the goods and services considered to be 'necessities' rather than 'luxuries' were a car for people living in areas without access to decent public transport, a one-week holiday in the UK, and a DVD player (Bradshaw et al., 2008).

Today, the way people live in **developed countries**, and increasingly the well-off in many parts of the world, creates demand for a much greater range of goods and services than just the bare necessities (even the list discussed in Activity 1.4 goes beyond this) or what can be bought on a minimum income. We not only demand what we *need* (e.g. food and shelter) but also what we *want* (e.g. mobiles phones, long-haul holidays, bottled water and fashionable clothes) and this inevitably leads to an increase in the production of goods and services.

45

For much of history, production and consumption by societies has changed local environments. The local impacts, from changing landscapes to use of resources and pollution, are usually the most obvious and of most concern. However, once trade developed between societies, humans began to have an impact on remote environments, whether by design or inadvertently (for example Hawaii). Today, increasing global demand for goods and services means that our influence on the environment is both widespread and intensifying. The desire for a pineapple affects life and people elsewhere.

4.1 Connected by the food we eat

Eating satisfies one of the bare (basic) necessities of life. However, in a developed country such as the UK eating is not simply a matter of survival. We can choose from a wide variety of affordable food from all over the world.

Activity 1.5　Where does your food come from?

This activity gets you to explore where the food you eat comes from – the results may surprise you.

So, try completing Table 1.2 by taking a look at food and drink

(a) that you have in your fridge and cupboards, and

(b) next time you go shopping.

To complete the table, select 10–15 items from the food and drink that you normally buy and consume.

The second column in the table is for writing the country of origin. Sometimes finding this out is quite straightforward, as you will find the information on the packaging, but you may have to use some further detective work for some items. For example, you may find the country of origin written on the large outer box that you can select vegetables from in a supermarket, or you could ask the shopkeeper.

You should spend approximately 15 minutes doing this activity.

Discussion

How did you get on? Were you surprised at what you found, or was it just what you were expecting?

A member of the course team tried this exercise and found that, in some cases, it was quite difficult to find out precisely where foods or ingredients for some food items came from, so he had to use 'intelligent guesswork'. He was also quite surprised by *how many* of the food and drink items had travelled a long way and from *how many different* countries the food originated.

Some examples of what he found that were unexpected: anchovy fillets from Morocco, brazil nuts from Bolivia, almonds from the USA, pasta from Australia, tinned tuna from the Maldives and blueberries from Israel.

Table 1.2 Where your food comes from	
Food or drink item (e.g. apples, bread, cheddar cheese, tinned tomatoes, chicken legs, wine)	Country of origin (if known) for majority ingredient of the food or drink (e.g. the flour in bread, chicken in a ready chicken meal)

The often limited information on the packaging gives only a measure of its journey from the country of origin. It does not give an indication of the total journey the food has made, which includes transport involved during its production and processing and its distribution to warehouse and shop, nor does it refer to the means of transport used.

Establishing the country of origin may not tell you the whole story of how far the food has travelled. Currently, one brand of king prawns (also known as Scampi), for example, are 'from the coastal waters of Britain and Ireland' as indicated by the UK packaging. But according to the company that markets them, they are frozen at sea and then shipped to Thailand, where they are shelled 'by hand'. The prawns are then shipped back to the UK – a 36 000 kilometre round trip.

This journey appears to defy common sense. What drives it is simple economics; the logic of the market place. The savings in labour costs from using workers in Thailand rather than the UK probably outweigh the extra cost of shipping the prawns around the world. Missing from the balance sheet, however, is the environmental cost of the journey. This is not usually charged to a company's accounts.

These unexpected journeys occur surprisingly often. If you had selected ice cream or caramels in your table, you could have chosen examples of products that apparently have travelled unnecessarily. The tonnages of caramels from Canada and ice cream from Germany and Sweden that are imported to the UK are the same as are exported from the UK.

4.2 The environmental impact of food

Trying to assess the environmental impact of food you are purchasing is difficult without knowing the whole story of its production, when it is not readily available. Consumers wishing to make ethical choices by reducing their environmental impact are often hindered by the lack of the necessary information.

If you live in the UK, British apples would seem to be a better choice in terms of energy expenditure than those from New Zealand. However, energy is required for effective long-term storage of apples harvested in the autumn in the UK. By the months of August and September, the amount of energy that has been used to store the British apples could be more than that required to ship them the 20 000 kilometres from New Zealand.

You have probably heard of the term 'food miles', which is frequently used in the media (the term 'food kilometres' hasn't caught on). It refers to the distance that food travels from the place of its production until it reaches the consumer. Given the media coverage of the debate surrounding the merits of purchasing foods freighted long distance or buying local foods, you might be under the impression that 'food miles' has the most significant environmental impact. However, it is only one small dimension. Over three-quarters of greenhouse gas emissions from the UK *food chain* comes from the production stages of food, which includes the processes involved in agriculture and fisheries, synthesis of fertilisers and pesticides, energy required for cold storage, food processing and packaging (DEFRA, 2007 p. 21).

In addition to greenhouse gas emissions, the production of food means that much of the world's land is used for agriculture, resulting in a direct environmental impact as forest and wetland habitats are cleared and the indigenous plants and animals are replaced by crops and livestock. Many millions of humans are involved in the process, whether on a subsistence level or as part of the international agricultural and food industry.

Kenya was one of the first African countries to develop systems in which high-value horticultural produce is exported to Europe. Figure 1.12 provides a summary of exports of green beans from Kenya.

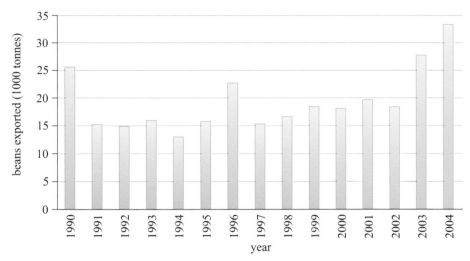

Figure 1.12 Kenyan export of green beans, including string beans
(Source: Jones, 2006)

Study note: bar charts

Bar charts are a specific type of graph. They are another way of representing numbers pictorially and can illustrate some pattern or trend in data. A bar chart is a diagram in which the numerical values of one or more variables are represented by the height or length of the rectangles. Whereas a line graph shows continuous data for all intervals or connects between the data points, as in the Keeling Curve, a bar chart is used for discrete intervals, e.g. data from every year. Bar charts are very effective for conveying the relative sizes of different quantities. Their particular strength, however, is enabling us to make comparisons.

In Figure 1.12 the heights of the bars represent the amount of green beans exported from Kenya, measured according to the scale used. For example, the height of the bar for the year 2001 is nearly 20, and the scale (on the vertical axis) is 1000 tonnes. So 20 × 1000 tonnes = 20 000 tonnes of green beans were exported from Kenya in 2001.

As with all types of graph, it does not tell you why the data is as it is, or offer any explanations. You will have noticed that there are considerable fluctuations, although the overall trend is upwards, i.e. increased exports, especially towards the end of the period shown.

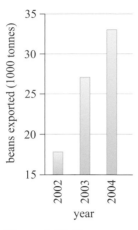

Figure 1.13 Kenyan export of green beans, including string beans, 2002–2004
(Source: Jones, 2006)

Study note: using data selectively to misrepresent

The bar chart in Figure 1.13 uses the same data as the one in Figure 1.12, but notice that the vertical scale does not start at zero as it did in the bar chart in Figure 1.12. Without studying the chart carefully you could be given the impression that the export of green beans has gone up by a multiple of about seven times between 2002 and 2004 and that exporting only started in 2002! Statistical data can be used very effectively in this way in order to try to misrepresent the picture.

SAQ 1.6   Exports of beans

(a) In Figure 1.12, which year had the lowest, and which the highest exports of Kenyan green beans?

(b) Approximately how many tonnes of green beans were exported in 2003? What was the increase in exports between 2003 and 2004?

Green beans are grown in the UK, but they have a limited harvest season and storing them is energy intensive. UK production fell by one-third between 1995 and 2005, whereas there was a fourfold increase in UK imports of green beans between 1990 and 2004. The amount of energy used in producing and transporting the green beans from Africa to the UK by air has been estimated by *life-cycle analysis* techniques to be 12 times greater than that for beans produced in EU countries. This suggests that air-freighting green beans from Africa is detrimental to the environment. This may be so, but there are other considerations. The livelihoods of many thousands of people in Africa from some of the poorest countries in the world depend on the continued demand in Europe for green beans throughout the year. If you buy air-freighted Kenyan beans you may be affecting the climate, but you are also supporting employment in Africa.

How has this situation come about, where food is flown thousands of miles even when it does not seem to be necessary? This is because food is produced, sold and bought as a commodity. In simple terms a commodity is something that is produced to be sold for profit, rather than needed by the people producing it. It is a long time since households in the developed world had to produce much of their own food, although this is still the case in many parts of *developing countries*. Once urbanisation began on a large scale, food was produced in the surrounding countryside and sold in the towns to people who had no land to grow it. Improvements in transport, storage methods and packaging since the nineteenth century have made a great difference to the variety of food available. Food bought and sold now comes from all over the world, where much production and distribution is in the hands of large, often multinational corporations and channelled through international markets. To give you an idea of the scale of some multinational companies, the world tea market is controlled by only three companies. The driving force in the food industry is economics, but until recently the food industry has not had to consider the environmental costs.

The explosive growth of commodity production is relatively recent in the case of food, and hence the effects of this on the environment have risen dramatically in a relatively short time.

4.3 Food – necessity or choice?

Having written Activity 1.5 *Where does your food come from?* I began to think more generally about the food I eat. Why do I choose a particular food or meal? My choices are usually based on a combination of habit, availability, price, health considerations, taste, ease of preparation and my family background and culture. I also try to reduce the negative effects (e.g. environmental impacts, animal welfare issues) of my choices, although I'm not always entirely sure of the nature and extent of these effects. What were the reasons for your choices of food? They'll probably be different from mine, but maybe you also consider environmental impacts, animal welfare and human exploitation concerns when you choose what to buy and eat.

Our current lifestyles, the way we live, are reflected in our choices and demand for food. Life in the UK would be quite different without trade with the rest of the world. Approximately 40% of all our food is imported into the UK and that includes many staples such as wheat as well as out-of-season vegetables and fruits. The once exotic pineapple or mango is available daily in supermarkets. Our world today is connected because, wherever you live, the food you eat and the goods and services you use come from all parts of the globe. This means that the decisions you and I make locally have global consequences, for societies and environments. A question we all have to face is whether we can continue our current lifestyles, or whether we might have to change the way we live to reduce our environmental impact. You may have already considered this question and have your own thoughts and opinions.

4.4 The journey so far

In this first part of the course you have been preparing to set out on a journey that will help you to make sense of, and respond to, a changing world. At this point you might like to reflect on how you are managing to tackle the course material so far: an important aspect of this journey is equipping yourself with some of the learning skills that I have introduced to you. Not only will this help you to get the most out of your studies as a more effective learner, it will also begin to prepare you for your written assignments.

As you have worked your way through Part 1 of this block you have been introduced to some of the ways in which lifestyles in the developed world are bringing about environmental change on a global scale. Your life and mine are connected to environmental changes around the world in many different ways. When I researched the contents of my fridge and shopping trolley I quickly found things that had come from almost every continent on the planet. My grandparents' generation would not even have heard of a good number of these foods. However, on the downside, they did not have to ponder on climate change as they sliced an air-freighted mango, or consider whether the meat in the chicken tikka masala was contributing to the loss of the world's biological diversity.

Our connected world is one of new hazards, where local actions can have global consequences. However, it is also a world of fascinating new knowledge and compelling ideas. Humans are beginning to apply to these problems some of the ingenuity that, many millennia ago, set them (us!) apart from all the other animals on the planet. The course will travel across this connected world in order to give you a good understanding of local and global environmental changes. By taking this journey you will be joining a community of students, researchers, architects, designers, activists, business and policy people who are applying creativity and energy to some of the greatest challenges of the age. You will get a better understanding of the processes behind environmental change. The journey will introduce you to ideas that claim to show a route to a more environmentally sustainable future, and you will come away with a better sense of how humanity might learn to live in a changing world.

Summary of Part 1

Part 1 has introduced you to the general skills of reading and evaluating written materials, and of reading and interpreting information from a variety of graphs, tables, charts and diagrams. Section 2 introduced the term 'environment'. It explored the complex nature of environmental issues and the variety of views held, and showed that even finding out information on a given issue is not straightforward. Section 3 visited Hawaii to discuss a key set of observations, the Keeling Curve, which monitors the increase of carbon dioxide in the atmosphere. It then looked at changes to biodiversity on the island and some reasons for these changes, before discussing ways of monitoring biodiversity globally. Section 4 discussed modern lifestyles and, by looking at changing patterns of food consumption and how food reaches us, raised the question of the environmental impacts of human activity.

After completing Part 1 you should:

- understand the concept of environment
- appreciate some of the interrelationships between humans and environment on a global scale
- be aware of the complexity of environmental issues and problems
- appreciate that information is written for a purpose and begin developing skills of reading and evaluating information presented in a variety of forms
- be able to read and interpret a graph and bar chart.

Answers to SAQs

SAQ 1.1

Many of the words used in this passage, like 'bogus' and 'play acting' are used for dramatic effect, and contain value judgements that might imply something is right, or wrong. This should not distract you from your task.

The last sentence of the first paragraph talks of 'a primeval jungle that is the dream of paradise'. However, the opening of the second paragraph says this is a bogus paradise, and it ends by saying the trees are play-acting. Fortey's message should be clear: the forest he encounters looks like an untouched 'primeval' jungle, but this is misleading. To put it another way, he is explaining that the native vegetation has mostly been replaced by introduced species.

SAQ 1.2

Introduction of new species:

The first paragraph describes how Polynesians introduced a large number of animal and plant species. Grazing animals, animals that escaped, such as rats and pigs, and any invasive plants come under this heading. You might also have identified the current nursery industry for tropical plants – if any of these have escaped, they become part of the bogus paradise described by Richard Fortey.

Habitat loss and degradation:

To create space for their agriculture the early settlers would have had to destroy native vegetation and habitats, and irrigation may well have modified other habitats. Logging for sandalwood has degraded or fragmented many forest habitats. Considerable land areas would have been cleared, and habitats destroyed, to make space for sugar plantations and commercial growing of pineapple, coffee and other crops.

SAQ 1.3

(a) All of the species pictured here belong to the animal kingdom (including corals, which I had to look up).

(b) The species least at risk of extinction are in the category 'vulnerable'. In Figure 1.10 only the White-headed vulture is described as vulnerable. The others are listed as either endangered or critically endangered. Note that these categories change over time as circumstances change: for many species the threats are increasing, but for some the threats decrease.

SAQ 1.4

(a) The animal kingdom has the largest number of identified species, with approximately 1.5 million species or about four-fifths of all those described. This is followed by the plant kingdom, with 300 000 species.

(b) 41 000 = 29 000 (animals) plus 12 000 (plants)

(c) 41 000 out of two million approximately. Using a calculator or mental arithmetic simplifies this proportion to two out of a hundred.

SAQ 1.5

(a) Fish have the largest number of identified species, 30 000.

(b) 9960 species of birds have been assessed by the IUCN, much more than for any other grouping.

(c) Birds top the list again. All (100%) identified species have been assessed. Note that a high percentage of mammals and amphibians have also been assessed.

(d) At first sight, the answer appears to be amphibians, with 1800 listed as threatened *by the IUCN*. However, some caution is needed when interpreting figures here. The number of species threatened refers to those that have been assessed, not those that are known. A high proportion of birds, mammals and amphibians have been assessed, so the number of their species threatened is likely to be close to the expected total. In the case of reptiles and fish, only a small proportion of known species have been assessed, so the number of species given as threatened represents only a partial total – which is why these figures have brackets. The information is not complete and there is no answer yet.

SAQ 1.6

(a) The lowest is 1994, being 13 000 tonnes, and the highest 2004, being 33 000 tonnes.

(b) About 27 000 tonnes were exported in 2003. The increase in exports between 2003 and 2004 is 33 000 minus 27 000 = 6 000 tonnes.

References

Adam, D. (2008) 'World carbon dioxide levels highest for 650,000 years, says US report', *The Guardian*, 13 May.

Bradshaw, J., Middleton, S., Davis, A., Oldfield, N., Smith, N., Cusworth, L. and Williams, J. (2008) *A Minimum Income Standard for Britain: What People Think*, Joseph Rowntree Foundation, July.

DEFRA (2007) *The Environment in your Pocket 2007*, London, Department for Environment, Food and Rural Affairs.

Delingpole, J. (2007) 'Polar bears in danger? Is this some kind of joke?', 12 November, http://www.timesonline.co.uk/tol/comment/columnists/guest_contributors/article2852551.ece (Accessed 11 August 2008).

EPI (2005) *Eco-Economy Indicators: FiSH DATA Wild Fish Catch Hits Limits: Oceanic Decline Offset by Increased Fish Farming*, Earth Policy Institute, http://www.earthpolicy.org/Indicators/Fish/Fish_data.htm#fig1 (Accessed 11 August 2008).

Fortey, R. (2005 [2004]) *The Earth: An Intimate History* (1st edn), London, Harper Perennial.

IUCN (2006) *IUCN Red List of Threatened Species,* Facts about Threatened Species, http://www.iucn.org/themes/ssc/redlist2006/threatened_species_facts.htm (Accessed 11 August 2008).

IUCN (2007a) *IUCN Red List of Threatened Species*, IUCN Red List Categories and Criteria, http://www.iucnredlist.org/info/categories_criteria (Accessed 11 August 2008).

IUCN (2007b) *IUCN Red List of Threatened Species*, Photo Gallery 2007, http://www.iucnredlist.org/info/gallery (Accessed 11 August 2008).

IUCN (2007c) *Summary Statistics for Globally Threatened Species*, Table 1, Numbers of threatened species by major groups of organisms (1996–2007), http://www.iucnredlist.org/info/stats (Accessed 11 August 2008).

IUCN (2007d) *IUCN Red List of Threatened Species*, Fighting the Extinction Crisis: Conservation in Action, http://www.iucn.org/themes/ssc/redlist2007/fighting_extinctioncrisis_2007.htm#hawaii (Accessed 11 August 2008).

Jones, A. (2006) *Fresh Insights Number 4 – A life cycle analysis of UK supermarket imported green beans from Kenya*, http://www.agrifoodstandards.net/en/filemanager/active?fid=68 (Accessed 5 August 2008).

Keeling, C. D. (1960) 'The concentrations and isotopic abundances of carbon dioxide in the atmosphere', *Tellus*, vol. 12, pp. 200–203.

Keeling, R. (2007) *Lessons from Mauna Loa: On the value of continuous time series*, Ralph Keeling Presentations, Scripps CO_2 Program, http://scrippsco2.ucsd.edu/talks/rfk_hawaii_mlo_50th.pdf (Accessed 11 August 2008).

McKenna, P. (2007) 'Climate myths: Polar bear numbers are increasing', http://www.newscientist.com/article/dn11656 (Accessed 11 August 2008).

Millennium Ecosystem Assessment (2005) *Ecosystems and Human Well-being: Synthesis Report*, Island Press, Washington DC.

Natural History Museum (2008) *National Biodiversity Network's Species Dictionary*, http://nbn.nhm.ac.uk/nhm/kingdoms.shtml (Accessed April 2008).

Scripps (2007a) *Mauna Loa Seasonally Adjusted*, Scripps CO_2 Program, Scripps Institution of Oceanography, http://scrippsco2.ucsd.edu/graphics_gallery/mauna_loa_record/mauna_loa_seasonally_adjusted.html, La Jolla, CA (Accessed October 2007).

Scripps (2007b) *Mauna Loa Record*, Scripps CO_2 Program, Scripps Institution of Oceanography, http://scrippsco2.ucsd.edu/graphics_gallery/mauna_loa_record/mauna_loa_record.html, La Jolla, CA (Accessed October 2007).

Part 2
Life in a changing world

Roger Blackmore and Joe Smith

Introduction

1

The focus of Part 2 is our dynamic and changing world. The first section considers what it means to think of the world in ecological terms. Section 2 takes a tour of the incredible history of the Earth and the life it supports by following its development from formation to the present day. Section 3 explores the contribution that *carbon* plays in maintaining a climate suitable for life, then investigates how the 'new kid on the block', humanity, is changing the planet's atmosphere and climate by altering carbon flows through different parts of the Earth. This raises the important question of how we can live in a way that does not harm our life-support system. The final section discusses the concept of sustainability and asks whether it has the power to change the way humanity understands and acts on the environmental challenges it faces.

1.1 Seeing the world *eco*-logically

What does it mean to look at the world ecologically? It is worth going back to the root of the prefix *eco*. It comes from the Greek *oikos*, meaning household, home or habitat, and *logos*, meaning word, now often stretched to indicate thought or meaning. It is no accident that the words economy and ecology share the same root. Both an *oekonomia* and an *oekologia* suggest a system of interacting, interdependent units. The term ecology technically refers to a branch of biology concerned with the science of the relationship between organisms and their environment. However, it is also used loosely as equivalent to the term 'environment'.

For this reason the prefix 'eco' has been exploited to suggest the environmental virtues of everything from washing liquids to cars. Eco-towns; eco-terrorists; eco-heroes; eco-kettle; eco-schools and eco-design: these two syllables have done a lot more work than the founders of the discipline of ecology in the late nineteenth century might have expected!

Although these varied uses of *eco* suggest that it isn't a precise term, they do show how many more people are thinking ecologically (in other words, they are thinking in terms of human organisms (or societies) and their environment or habitat). Sociologists have studied the growth of this kind of thinking – usually tagged environmentalism – since its period of very rapid growth in the early 1970s. Local concerns at the pollution caused by the fast-paced development of the post-second-world-war era, and the arrival of photographs of the Earth from space, taken by the first astronauts, generated a new kind of politics. The concept of *oikos* had been borrowed from environmental scientists and, through inventive campaigning, given a resonance and urgency that would have far-reaching consequences.

The environmentalist groups of the 1970s, such as Greenpeace and Friends of the Earth, were often rooted in environmental science. Nevertheless, the campaigners spliced that knowledge together with media and political campaigning skills. Non-violent direct action, or civil disobedience, has also frequently been part of their work. Hence images of heroic action against whaling or rainforest destruction became a central part of how people think about environmentalism. However, one of the most popular images that summarises the growth of 'eco-thinking' in North America in the 1970s was a Native American (in fact a Hollywood actor of Italian descent, see Figure 2.1) who in one TV advertisement was portrayed shedding a tear at the sight of the pollution that was despoiling 'his' land. This and other environmentalist campaigning borrowed from Native American culture in order to reinforce their own arguments about seeking a society that could live in harmony with nature. Anthropologists and historians have since criticised this clichéd account of Native American cultures and their relations with their environments, but the 'borrowings' had already done their work. The glycerine tear used in that particular advert nicely summarises the way that environmentalists have worked to build up and channel a body of public concern through emotive images and words.

Figure 2.1 Iron Eyes Cody, a Hollywood 'Indian' who appeared in a TV ad crying a (glycerine) tear at the polluting of his pristine land

Despite the slickness of some of their campaigning techniques, environmentalism has always been rooted in very real concerns about serious problems at both local and global levels. Modern economics, politics and culture are rooted in a long period of very successful exploitation of the Earth around us. The Earth has been treated as if it were limitless: either as endless sources of raw materials or bottomless pits that could contain waste. The startling economic success – and consequent impact – of humans as a species can be illustrated by the figures in Table 2.1 summarising human impacts on the planet in the twentieth century.

Table 2.1 A summary of some key changes of the last century that have driven environmental change	
Item	**Change factor 1890s–1990s**
World population	4×
Total world urban population	13×
Industrial output	40×
Energy use	13×
Coal production	7×
Carbon dioxide emissions	17×
Water use	9×
Marine fish catch	35×
Cattle population	4×
Pig population	9×
Irrigated area	5×
Blue whale population (Southern Ocean)	0.0025 × (for every 1000 there are now only two or three)
Forest area	0.8 × (reduced by one-fifth)

Adapted from O'Neill, J. (2000) Something New Under the Sun: An environmental history of the twentieth century, London, Penguin, pp. 360–361.

The way people read this table varies depending upon their foremost interests and concerns. An economist or business person might quickly focus on the fact that industrial output is 40 times as big as in 1890, indicating wealth creation and poverty alleviation. Environmentalists in turn would bemoan the immense growth in energy use and carbon dioxide emissions, the industrial scale of fishing, and the loss of species such as whales and habitats such as rainforests. Those concerned primarily with social justice would note that the economic gains have not been evenly distributed amongst the growing global population, and would want to add to the table some statistics about persistent poverty and inequality of opportunity.

This table was constructed by a historian, John O'Neill, the author of a history of the twentieth century told from an environmental perspective. He acknowledges that some of the numbers are more reliable than others. There are also some very startling numbers that don't appear here at all, such as the fact that in 1900 there were just over 4000 passenger cars; one hundred years later there were well over 450 million on the road. However, the overall impression is clear. The last one hundred years or so have seen a dramatic increase in the demands that humanity makes upon the Earth on which it depends.

Activity 2.1 Changes to the place where you live

Take a few minutes to relate some of the statistics in Table 2.1 to the place where you live – whether it's a town or city, a village or another kind of community. How are the figures reflected in tangible changes that you can see in the buildings and streets around you? This might relate to the age, nature or number of buildings and vehicles; the layout of roads and paths; the vehicles; or the kinds of services (e.g. water, energy and communications) supplied to the houses and flats.

Discussion

I have a 1912 photo of the street I live in stuck to my office wall (Figure 2.2(a)), which makes some changes easy to spot. The roadworks in the foreground of the modern photo (Figure 2.2(b)) show the Victorian water supply system being renewed. The buildings look cleaner now that sooty coal fires are a thing of the past in cities. There is a dramatic contrast between the couple of carts (and liberal sprinkling of horse manure) and the rows of parked cars filling the left-hand side of the street today. In place of the handful of gas lamps distributed along the road there are electric lights on the outside of most houses, as well as plenty of street lighting. The walls of the houses are now peppered with satellite dishes, aerials and telephone cables, and the mottled pavements show signs of plenty of piped services including gas, electricity, water and media cables going into every home. The streets are marked with road signs, cycle paths and lines in an effort to discipline the very large numbers of road users. Among the delivery vehicles are the supermarket home shopping services – an echo of the butcher's boy on his bike or milk horse and cart of a century earlier? These days the diesel van will be delivering a dizzying array of food, drinks and goods from around the world that would have astonished Queen Victoria, whose hothouse pineapples were considered rare treasures. The string of private cars hints at some of the environmental challenges (including future oil shortages, carbon dioxide emissions and air pollution) generated by wealth and technological change.

However, there is also a positive environmental note: with a close-up photo you would be able to see that many of the railings are cluttered with bicycles. In Cambridge, there are plenty of student bed-sits in the street, and the city's size, parking restrictions and the town's universities' regulations favour cycling over private transport. Once a week the pavement is crowded with a huge number of wheelie bins – reflecting an enormous growth in household waste. Yet you might also spot one or two of the kerbside recycling scheme boxes and new (alternate week) green wheelie bins for compostable waste – one of the most recent introductions to the streetscape.

(a)

(b)

**Figure 2.2: (a) Bateman Street, Cambridge in 1912: spot the horse dung;
(b) Bateman Street, Cambridge in 2008: spot the difference**

1.2 Imagining the world from space

Environmentalists have applied their communications and campaigning skills to promote an 'ecological' frame of thought. However, the ecological thought would not have been popularised without a basis in authoritative science. Most progress in science is based on careful observation and the thorough testing of ideas by experiment and further observation, the approach illustrated by Charles Keeling in Part 1. Sometimes, however, individuals take a leap of imagination that changes the way we see the world. Here is the story of one such scientist.

If you are unfamiliar with the description of chemical elements and compounds, or feel the need to refresh your memory, read through Box 2.1

Box 2.1   The chemical elements

Every object on Earth is made of chemical *elements*. Most elements were created in the nuclear furnaces of exploding stars in the early Universe. We and the Earth around us are made literally from stardust! There are 109 named elements, of which 92 occur naturally on Earth. Many will be familiar, such as carbon and oxygen. Of the known elements, up to 30 are believed to be essential to the survival of living organisms. Some of these are listed here. Each element can be represented by a chemical symbol of one or two letters, a shorthand form of its current name or, sometimes, its Latin name. The smallest recognisable part of a chemical element is called an *atom*. Here are some common examples:

Element	Symbol
carbon	C
hydrogen	H
oxygen	O
nitrogen	N
calcium	Ca
phosphorus	P
sulphur	S
sodium	Na
iron	Fe

Thus C stands for carbon, and Ca for calcium, but Fe refers to *ferrum*, the Latin name for iron, and Na to *natrium*, Latin for sodium.

Where conditions are suitable for life, few elements exist as single atoms. Elements are usually found combined together, either with other atoms of the same element, or with atoms of other elements to make *compounds*. There is an enormous range of possible combinations of different elements and therefore an enormous number of chemical compounds. The smallest amount or building block of any substance we encounter, compound or element, comprising two or more atoms, is called a *molecule*.

The symbols of the elements are put together to give the formula of a compound. For example, hydrogen and oxygen combine to make water, which has the formula H_2O. The number 2 indicates that two atoms of hydrogen combine with one atom of oxygen to make one molecule of water. The subscript number refers to the element it follows, so for H_2O the 2 refers to hydrogen, not oxygen. In contrast, a number before the formula refers to the number of individual molecules. For example, $3H_2O$ indicates three molecules of water.

Another example is carbon dioxide, which is mentioned frequently in this course because of its importance as a greenhouse gas in the atmosphere. It is a compound of carbon and oxygen with the formula CO_2, meaning one carbon atom combined with two oxygen atoms.

Methane is another naturally occurring greenhouse gas. It is a compound of carbon and hydrogen with the formula CH_4, meaning one carbon atom combined with four hydrogen atoms.

Finally, each element has an atomic mass associated with it. For convenience these are usually given as the *relative* atomic masses. Using this convention, the relative atomic mass of hydrogen is 1, carbon 12, and oxygen 16. A simple calculation shows that carbon dioxide, CO_2, has a relative molecular mass of 44 $(12 + (16 \times 2))$, compared with 12 for carbon. Put another way, 44 kg of carbon dioxide contains 12 kg of carbon.

In the early 1960s, the United States government gave NASA (the National Aeronautics and Space Administration) the task of exploring space, and getting a man on the moon before the Russians. Part of its remit was to search for life on other planets. If life exists elsewhere, how could it be detected? The answer came from an unorthodox British scientist working for NASA. He reasoned as follows: the Earth's atmosphere consists mostly of nitrogen and oxygen. This is unusual because oxygen is a highly reactive gas: it tends to react with most other elements or compounds found on the planet (iron rusts and charcoal burns in the presence of oxygen). Over the hundreds of millions of years of the Earth's life any oxygen in the atmosphere should have been removed by combining with other elements to form stable compounds. Its existence in the atmosphere can only mean one thing: it is being regenerated continually by living organisms. To look for life on another planet such as Mars, therefore, we should look for signs that its atmosphere contains unstable gases like oxygen.

Figure 2.3 James Lovelock, inventor of the electron capture device and Gaia proponent

In Greek mythology, Gaia is the goddess who represents the Earth

The scientist's suggestion was soon put to the test when new observations from telescopes showed that the atmospheres of both Venus and Mars were composed almost entirely of stable gases, mostly carbon dioxide. Despite this discovery the Mars mission went ahead, because the search for life wasn't its only motivation. Fifty years on, scientists are still searching Mars for the conditions that might support life, now or in the past. The scientist was James Lovelock (Figure 2.3), who later, with his collaborator the American biologist Lynn Margulis, developed the Gaia hypothesis of a living, self-regulating world.

Lovelock was born near London in 1919. He didn't thrive at school and left to work as a laboratory assistant in a small chemical firm. He took evening classes to study chemistry, before gaining a first degree at Manchester University. He then worked for twenty years at the National Institute for Medical Research in London, where he was allowed freedom to follow his own ideas. Among his many inventions was the electron capture device in 1957, a measuring instrument capable of detecting the tiniest amounts of trace gases. Its use aided the discovery of pesticide residues in the environment, described in Rachel Carson's influential book *Silent Spring* (Carson, 1962), and later established the widespread presence of **CFCs** in the atmosphere (the compounds responsible for damaging the ozone layer). In 1961, while in the USA, he was invited by NASA to join a team at the Jet Propulsion Laboratory, working for its space exploration programme. It was while working there that he formed his hypothesis about Gaia.

> One afternoon in 1965 at the JPL, when thinking of these facts, the thought came to me in a flash that such constancy [of the atmosphere] required the existence of an active control system. At that time I lacked any idea of the nature of the control system, except that the organisms on the Earth's surface were part of it.
>
> (*Lovelock, 1992*)

The Gaia concept is controversial. It also has a variety of interpretations, from the idea that organisms on Earth have altered its composition to the stronger view that the Earth's biosphere itself behaves as though it were a single, living organism. Critics would say that it is more a way of thinking about a complex system than a scientific theory. Nevertheless, the idea that life has shaped and still shapes our planetary environment is now broadly accepted. It has influenced the emerging discipline of Earth Systems science, which views our planet as a complex, interacting system. It studies the main components of the planet – the atmosphere, oceans, fresh water, rocks, soils and biosphere – and, crucially, the interactions between these components (Lawton, 2001).

> The start of the Gaia hypothesis was the view of the Earth from space, revealing the planet as a whole but not in detail.
>
> (*Lovelock, quoted in Turney, 2003*)

These words from Lovelock provide a suitable introduction to the next section, but so also does this warning from Sir Crispin Tickell, in a 2006 lecture:

> It was, I think, Lynn Margulis who described Gaia [life on Earth] as 'a tough bitch'. So she is. Over 3.8 billion years, it is her robustness which is so impressive and reassuring. She has survived the great extinctions from outside the Earth, and the great catastrophes from within it. This has required a remarkable resilience whereby physical and biological mechanisms have adapted to new circumstances.
>
> Gaia is a lady who has remained broadly the same underneath, but can wear many clothes for many weathers and many fashions. She has no particular tenderness for humans. We are no more than a small, albeit immodest, part of her. Only in the last tick of the clock of geological time did humans make their appearance, and only in the last fraction of it did they make any impact on the earth system as a whole.
>
> *(Tickell, 2006)*

2   Earth story: a walk through deep time

> The world is but a perennial movement. All things in it are in constant motion – the earth, the rocks of the Caucasus, the pyramids of Egypt – both with the common motion and with their own. Stability itself is nothing but a more languid motion. I cannot keep my subject still. It goes along befuddled and staggering, with a natural drunk[en]ness.
>
> *(Montaigne, quoted in Zweig, 1981)*

For the past ten thousand years the Earth's climate has been remarkably stable. It is probably no accident that during this period, human societies have learned how to practise agriculture and build cities and states, and civilisations and empires have risen and fallen. Yet for much of our planet's long geological history its atmosphere would not have supported the current diversity of life, and the shape and position of its continents would be quite unrecognisable today. Our planetary home has experienced long periods of almost tropical warmth, with no ice at the poles, and times when considerable portions of its landmasses lay under deep ice. An appreciation of the Earth's history can help bring perspective to global environmental changes occurring today; for example, to climate change and biodiversity loss.

2.1 Geological time

The Earth formed with the rest of the solar system approximately 4600 million years ago, and its evolution has played out over vast timescales that we find very hard to grasp. Geologists divide the Earth's history into key time intervals based on their interpretations of rock formations and their fossil records. Box 2.2 describes the main divisions.

Our planet may be ancient, but much of the understanding of its history has been pieced together only in the last fifty years. This section does not set out to explain the processes that have guided its development over geological timescales, or the recent theories and methods that have helped to uncover them. This is a rapidly developing field, where interpretations are being contested and new theories advanced. The purpose of this section is to give you an overview of how scientists believe the Earth has developed, and to describe some of the key events of its history.

2.2 Deep time

Geologists are familiar with working with intervals of a million years or more, but to most ordinary beings whose attention is focused on getting through the day it can be hard to consider what the world would be like ten

Box 2.2   Geological time

The geological equivalents of hours, minutes and seconds are *eons*, *eras* and *periods*. The longest intervals are eons, followed by eras, which are then subdivided into geological periods. Periods can be further subdivided into epochs, although these are rarely used in this section. There are many different systems for describing geological time; for example, some avoid the term eon, preferring in their place to use only eras.

Unlike conventional time, geological intervals do not have the same length. Each eon, era and period was originally marked by a major change in the geological record that indicated a key change in developments at the Earth's surface. Thus, the boundaries between one geological age and another are associated with major changes to the Earth's climate, its atmosphere, or key stages in the evolution of life. These changes often occur together. However, the timing given for specific events is often adjusted as methods of dating improve.

A key transition for early geologists was the first appearance of fossils in rocks of the Cambrian period. Each geological period after the Cambrian described changes in the fossil record, whereas the time before it was known as the 'pre-Cambrian'. This boundary, about 550 million years ago, now separates the Cryptozoic eon from the Phanerozoic eon. These two intervals have impressive-sounding names, but they mean simply 'time of hidden life' and 'time of visible life' respectively.

or a hundred years ahead. Our own lifespan and those of our parents and children limit our time horizons. John McPhee, a lyrical American science writer, coined the term *deep time* to describe these almost unimaginable timescales, and said of them:

> … events so glued in the slowness of mineral time that they annihilate the scale of our lives and furnish convincing images of eternity.

> (McPhee, quoted in Zweig, 1981)

In an attempt to bring some human scale to 'deep time', I am going to take you on an imaginary journey as a time traveller, where distance travelled represents deep time. In this scenario, imagine you are walking along a track, maybe a disused railway, but the journey could be anywhere of the length chosen – ninety kilometres. I imagined walking along a sandy beach, hence the title of the next section.

Study note: reading for understanding

The story of the Earth's history presented here is necessarily a simplified one; even so, some detailed information is presented. It is there to provide you with a picture of some of the richness of the Earth's history. However, you are not required to remember all the details. Treat this material as a celebration of our planet and of the skills of scientists in unravelling some of its secrets. Read it with the aim of identifying the main changes that have occurred to the Earth over its long history. With that in mind, look out for summaries at the beginning and end of sections, and keep an eye on the timelines of the two tables.

2.3 Footsteps in the sand

Imagine, then, that ninety kilometres of sandy beach represent the 4600 million years of the Earth's history. This means that for every kilometre travelled approximately 50 million years of deep time pass. A reasonably fit walker can manage twenty kilometres a day, so the story of Earth can be told in a journey of four and a half days. You, the time traveller, will 'walk' a thousand million (a billion) years each day.

Table 2.2 is the guide for the overall journey through deep time. It shows the main geological intervals and a timeline for some of the key events in the Earth's history. Until quite recently, very little was known of the events encountered on the first four days of the journey, particularly the earliest times. Many of the dates given are only approximate; dating an event to an accuracy of 100 million years over a timescale of 4600 million, for example, is quite demanding. The geological record for the last half day of the journey, covering the Phanerozoic eon, is known in more detail, though there is still plenty of uncertainty about the timing and interpretation of events.

Study note: reading the signposts

There are many ways in which writers provide 'signposts' to the reader, to guide them through material. One way is to use words to indicate the order or sequence of events, like 'first', 'second', 'next' and 'finally'. Because the following section describes in some detail the events of a timeline, there are plenty of examples of such signposting. In addition, there are subheadings with numbered days to help you keep track of where you are.

Nevertheless, a description of an imaginary journey is not always the easiest to follow. The passages below covering days 1 to 4 are interrupted occasionally with descriptions of the geological evidence for some of the events seen on the journey. The author uses descriptive words such as 'traces', 'remains', 'deposits' and 'geological record' to indicate a switch from the journey to the evidence. You can use techniques like these in your own writing to make your meaning clear.

Table 2.2 The geological timeline

Geological time period		Millions of years ago (My)	Event
Eon	**Era**		
		Day 1	
Hadean		4600	Formation of planet Earth Early Sun weaker than today
		Day 2	
Archaean		3600	Earliest evidence of life (bacteria)
		3600–3100	Early oceans, then continents form
		3000	First appearance of cyanobacteria, or blue-green algae
		2500	Atmosphere still has high concentrations of carbon dioxide and methane Oxygen is found only as a trace gas
		Days 3 and 4	
Proterozoic		2500–700	Oxygen slowly increases, first in the atmosphere then in the ocean
		850–500	A snowball Earth? A major age of ice
		700–545	Ocean oxygenated Multicellular life develops in oceans
		Day 5	
Phanerozoic	Palaeozoic	545	Diversity of life increases markedly and spreads to land, punctuated by extinction events
		Day 5, kilometres 6–9	
	Mesozoic	250	Major extinction Great continent Pangaea forms Age of dinosaurs
		The final kilometre	
	Cenozoic	65	Major extinction Mammals replace dinosaurs Humans appear

2.3.1 Days 1 and 2

The first two days of the journey cover the time interval of the Hadean and Archaean eons. The journey begins on day one with the Earth newly formed. The early Earth would have been hostile territory for any form of life, with frequent meteor strikes, considerable volcanic activity and no ozone layer to protect life from the Sun's harmful radiation. Even though the early Sun was cooler than today, the early Earth would have been too hot for comfort. For this reason, this initial phase of the Earth's history is sometimes called the Hadean eon, after Hades, the Greek term for the underworld or hell. For the whole of the first day, the first twenty kilometres representing 1000 million years, no life appears on Earth.

Bacteria represent one of the five kingdoms of life discussed in Part 1

The first life on Earth, bacteria, appear early in the journey, on day two. The earliest traces of life found today are bacteria preserved as tiny patterns in a rock formation known as *chert*, which has been dated to 3600 million years ago. The bacteria lived in the newly formed oceans which provided the environment for early life and, indeed, for life for much of Earth's history. Early continents appear during the first half of the second day, a sign that deep in the Earth the mechanisms that build continents, mountain ranges and ocean deeps have begun (Stanley, 2005).

Throughout these first two days of the journey, carbon dioxide and methane dominate the atmosphere of the Hadean and Archaean eons. Both atmosphere and ocean are without significant amounts of oxygen and would be unable to support most life present today on Earth. However, bacteria are beginning to affect the atmosphere by releasing nitrogen, and, halfway through day two (3000 million years ago), *cyanobacteria* or blue-green algae appear. This is a key event for life on Earth, because these organisms are capable of *photosynthesis* (discussed in Section 3) and produce oxygen; they begin slowly to change the Earth's atmosphere forever. The remains of the ancient algae can be seen in mound-like formations called *stromatolites*, formed from mats of threadlike bacteria and sediment (Figures 2.4a and 2.4b). They look like very large molehills, but have often been flattened by eons of erosion. Blue-green algae still flourish in lakes and oceans in today's world.

By the end of the first two days' journey, nearly half of the Earth's history has passed by. The first oceans and continents have formed and life, in the form of bacteria, now populates the oceans and slowly begins to transform the atmosphere.

2.3.2 Days 3 and 4

The next two days of the journey are through the Proterozoic eon, or time of early life. This eon, which lasts from 2500 to 545 million years ago, spans almost another half of Earth's history. It can be thought of as the time when early life – cyanobacteria – helped create an oxygen-rich atmosphere, but also diversified into more complex forms.

During the third day's journey, the effect of photosynthesis by cyanobacteria and similar organisms is to increase oxygen in the atmosphere. This process, slow at first, appears to reach a threshold or tipping point by the middle of day three (2200 to 2000 million years ago). It is likely that much of the oxygen first released to the atmosphere is initially absorbed by the abundant iron- and sulphur-bearing rocks at the surface. Oxygen only reaches significant levels in the atmosphere when these rocks have been transformed into oxygen-rich minerals. This event is marked in the geological record by the sudden ending of *banded iron* formations (Figure 2.4c), still the source of most iron ore today, and their replacement by red, oxygen-rich iron-bearing rocks. As John McPhee puts it:

… pale-green ferrous iron, which exists everywhere, in fully five percent of crustal rock [becomes] red in the shales of New Jersey, red in the sandstones of Yunan, red in the banks of the Volga, red in the Solway Firth.

(McPhee, quoted in Zweig, 1981)

The 'banded iron' layers form only in oceans – banding or layering is a sign of deposition in water. The presence of these deposits early in the geological record is evidence of a lack of oxygen in the ancient oceans. In later deposits iron compounds combined with oxygen to form un-banded, red-coloured minerals. The disappearance of 'banded iron' layers is therefore a sign that the oceans have taken up oxygen from the atmosphere.

(a)

(b)

(c)

(d)

Figure 2.4 Signs from the past: (a) well-preserved stromatolites from the Cambrian era; (b) living stromatolites in western Australia; (c) banded iron; (d) an early tillite deposit with a characteristic mix of broken rock and other debris

This major change to the atmosphere can be linked to two other changes. First, together with other factors, it reduces the amount of carbon dioxide in the atmosphere and removes the methane. The lessening of these greenhouse gases allows the climate to cool. There are tentative signs that about this time there occurred a period of global glaciation, a spread of glaciers and ice sheets over continents and oceans. This is the first time that such an event occurs, but for the rest of the Earth's history similar cold periods occur from time to time.

The effect of greenhouse gases, such as carbon dioxide and methane, on climate is discussed in the next section

Protista, fungi, plants and animals are the other four kingdoms of life discussed in Part 1

The second change is that an oxygen-rich environment appears to favour more complex forms of life than bacteria. The timing and rates of change of these transitions are still a matter for debate and research, but during the fourth day of the journey early examples of the other four kingdoms of life, protista, fungi, plants and animals, make an appearance. This new life is characterised by a cell where the *genetic* material is contained within a nucleus, leading to the possibility of sexual reproduction and an acceleration of evolution. It also allows different *cells* to have different functions, leading to the multicellular life of fungi, plants and animals. As the Proterozoic eon ends, multicellular life such as worms and jellyfish makes an appearance in the now oxygen-rich oceans. There is also another major spread of glaciation and ice over continents and oceans, towards the end of day four, that some have called the snowball Earth. The signs of past glaciations are provided by deposits of ancient *tillites* (Figure 2.4d), uneven jumbles of broken boulders, sand and mud deposited by glaciers.

You have now travelled 80 of the 90-kilometre journey. At this point, you would still not recognise the continents on the surface of the Earth, and most life remains in the oceans. This life generally has no hard bony or skeletal material, so the few remains that it leaves for geologists to find take skill to interpret. Nevertheless, conditions are now ripe for an explosion of life on Earth.

SAQ 2.1 Looking for evidence

The interpretation of the early development of the Earth is based partly on the examination of some of the oldest rocks on Earth. Assuming the dating is correct, in Sections 2.3.1 and 2.3.2 *four* examples of rocks have been used as geological evidence for the key changes on the Earth. List the rocks and the key changes for which they provide evidence.

2.3.3 Day 5

The last day's journey is shorter, only 11 kilometres, but the pace of change quickens: major events occur at almost every kilometre and many of them are marked by a new division of deep time, either an era or a period. It covers a span of approximately 550 million years or just over a tenth of Earth's history, and three geological eras: the Palaeozoic, Mesozoic and Cenozoic, or old, middle and modern eras. As you journey through the time of visible life, the Phanerozoic eon, many new varieties of life on Earth appear and disappear. For this last day Table 2.3 provides a more detailed guide. Here, the narrative will focus on the evolution of life and the rise and fall of different groups of species, and where possible relate this to changes to the atmosphere, oceans, and geography of the Earth.

Table 2.3 The timeline of visible life, the Phanerozoic eon

Geological time period			Event
Era	Period	Millions of years ago (My)	
		Day 5	
Palaeozoic	Cambrian	545	Marine animals with hard skeletal parts appear
	Cambrian/ Ordovician		Photosynthesis by plants and weathering of rocks lead to increased oxygen and nitrogen in the atmosphere
		Kilometres 3–4	
	Silurian	440	First major extinction Second ice age
	Silurian/ Devonian	430	Major invasion of land by plants and animals
		Kilometres 5–6	
	Carboniferous	350	Second major extinction Third ice age
	Carboniferous/ Permian	325–275	Carbon burial leads to a fourth and greatest ice age
		Kilometre 7	
Mesozoic	Triassic	250	Third and most destructive extinction Supercontinent Pangaea forms
		Kilometres 8–10	
	Jurassic/ Cretaceous	200	Dinosaurs appear and develop widely Earliest (small) mammals appear
		80	Pangaea begins to disperse Spread of flowering plants
		Kilometre 11 (approx.) The last kilometre	
Cenozoic		65	Fourth mass extinction event, associated with a major meteor impact
		600 metres to go	
		30	Global cooling and drying begins
		400 metres to go	
		20	Indian subcontinent meets Asia
		150 metres to go	
		6–4	First appearance of hominids
		40 metres to go	
	Quaternary	1.8 to recent	The last ice age begins
	Epoch	Years ago	
		4 metres to go	
		200 000 (approx.)	First appearance of early humans
		The final footstep	
	Holocene	11 000	Rise of agriculture, cities and states
	Anthro-pocene?	200	Industrial production increases. Global warming begins. Sixth extinction begins?

A mass extinction refers to the loss of a significant proportion of the world's species (and higher groupings of species) over a comparatively short geological time of a few million years, equivalent to a few dozen paces on our walk through deep time. There is no commonly agreed definition of a mass extinction, but most authorities identify five or six mass extinctions in the last 500 million years

By the start of the fifth day all of the five major divisions of life, the five kingdoms, have now evolved. The journey opens in the Palaeozoic Cambrian period with the 'Cambrian explosion', made famous by the extraordinary diversity of marine life found in the Burgess Shales, high up in the Canadian Rocky Mountains. Animals with hard skeletons or shells, for example trilobites, appear in the ocean for the first time. In the right circumstances, their remains are preserved in the rocks as fossils, and their sudden appearance in many places of the world is why this slice of deep time is known as the time of visible life. After a kilometre, trilobites start to suffer extinctions, but early reef-building corals and sponges appear and the first *vertebrates*, jawless fish, appear. Then, at the end of the second kilometre, the first major *mass extinction* occurs, coinciding with a major continental glaciation or *ice age*.

However, after no more than a few hundred metres into the Silurian period, plants and animals finally 'emerge' from the oceans and begin to colonise the land, joining fungi, bacteria and algae. Now all kingdoms of life have finally expanded beyond their birthplace in the oceans. This event is a major step for evolution; life flourishes now on land and in fresh water as well as in the oceans. It leads to increased rates of photosynthesis, and many other processes that exist today to maintain high levels of oxygen in the air and the ozone layer high above (that protects exposed life from the Sun's harmful radiation).

(a)

(b)

Figure 2.5 Early life in the fossil record: (a) Burgess Shale trilobite; (b) Wanneria trilobite, both from the Cambrian period

By the fourth kilometre of day five, in the Devonian period, life is flourishing in shallow tropical seas, and predators now include jawed fish, some the size of today's sharks. On land, the first vertebrate animals appear, and plants similar to mosses and ferns have taken to swampy areas. Some develop into large trees, forming the first forests. At the end of the fourth kilometre, marking the boundary of the Devonian and Carboniferous periods, a second mass extinction occurs, this time as a prolonged series of extinctions that eliminated about 70% of all species. The cause or causes are unclear although, again, it probably coincided with a colder period when large ice sheets formed near the poles.

The next kilometre takes us through the Carboniferous period, when the first winged insects and amphibians appear. Warmth returns quickly and early forests flourish in humid, swampy conditions. When they die, many of the dead trees and plants are preserved in the swamps and are slowly transformed into the largest coal deposits found today. As explained in Section 3, this 'burial' process also removes carbon from the atmosphere, leading to a sharp reduction of carbon dioxide in the atmosphere, which cools the climate. It is a likely cause of a series of major glaciations that occur later and last for many tens of millions of years. The Palaeozoic era ends at the end of the sixth kilometre with the most destructive mass extinction ever seen: estimates suggest that approximately 95% of all marine species and 70% of land species became extinct. It is known that most of the oceans lost their oxygen at this time, which would have been deadly. The causes of this are not clear, though the loss of oxygen is a sign that any oxygen that might be dissolved in the surface waters of the oceans is no longer being transported to their depths, a sign that the movement of deep ocean currents has been interrupted. This event coincides with periods of extensive volcanic activity in what is now Siberia, and also marks the coming together of the Earth's major landmasses to form a single supercontinent called Pangaea, meaning 'whole Earth', shown in Figure 2.6(a). Both events may have affected the climate significantly.

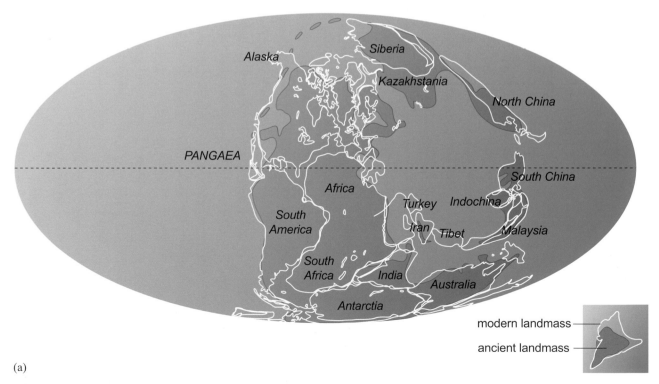

(a)

Figure 2.6(a) Map of the Earth showing the shape and distribution of its continents 255 million years ago
(Source: adapted from Scotese, 2008)

Life, however, recovers and diversifies again. For the next four kilometres, you pass through the Mesozoic era, the 'middle era' of deep time. Reptiles and small mammals appear early in the era and the first birds arrive towards the end, but the Mesozoic era is most notable for the rise of dinosaurs. After one kilometre, at the end of the Triassic and into the Jurassic period, dinosaurs become the dominant land vertebrates and continue to evolve and dominate throughout the middle era, a time span of 150 million years. It is a time of global warmth: temperatures are maybe 5 °C higher than today and the polar regions are free of ice. Most of the Earth's landmasses remain locked together in the supercontinent Pangaea, and some of its land areas far from oceans become dry zones and deserts. In the plant kingdom, seed-bearing plants and trees, including tree ferns and conifers, appear early on, and are more able to adapt to drier conditions. By the end of the era, in the Cretaceous period, flowering plants appear. Flowering plants, including trees, can also adapt to most conditions; by producing seeds rapidly and efficiently they are quick to colonise new areas. They provide us today with almost all our food crops. Meanwhile, the supercontinent splits up and begins to disperse into the modern continents, but the map of the world shown in Figure 2.6(b) would not look quite right yet, because the continents are distributed differently across the globe. Antarctica is still connected to Australasia and the Indian subcontinent is a long way south of the rest of Asia.

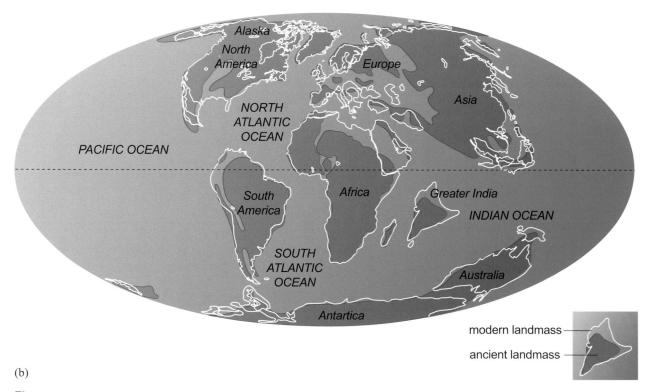

(b)

Figure 2.6(b) Map of the Earth showing the shape and distribution of its continents 65 million years ago
(Source: adapted from Scotese, 2008)

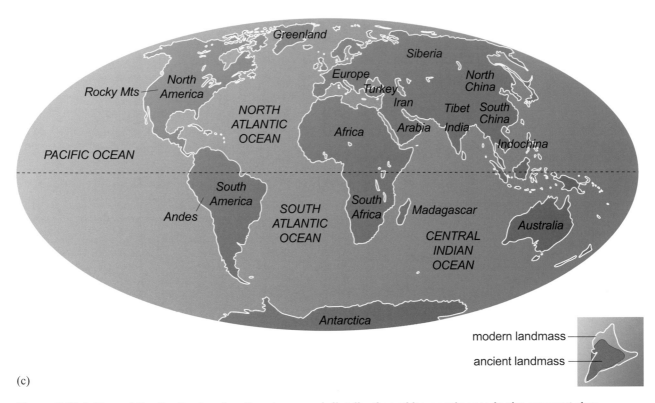

(c)

Figure 2.6(c) Map of the Earth showing the shape and distribution of its continents in the present day
(Source: adapted from Scotese, 2008)

The 'modern era' of deep time, or Cenozoic era, is ushered in quite literally with a bang as you approach the final kilometre of your 90-kilometre journey. Another mass extinction occurs, caused in part at least by a large asteroid strike that formed a crater off the Yucatan Peninsula in Mexico. Massive volcanic eruptions occur at the same time in parts of India. The extinctions affect dinosaurs particularly, while the subsequent evolution of mammals leads them to become the dominant land vertebrates.

As you draw closer to the present day, the finishing line of your journey through deep time, it makes sense to mark the final stages in terms of distance from the finishing line rather than the beginning. The modern era, then, begins 65 million years ago, with somewhat more than a kilometre of the journey to go.

For much of the Cenozoic era the climate is warmer than today, and levels of carbon dioxide are higher than recent values. Near the halfway mark, about 600 metres from the finishing line, carbon dioxide levels fall and the climate begins to cool. The Antarctic moves away from Australasia and is surrounded for the first time by the deep waters of the Southern Ocean, allowing ice sheets to develop. At 400 metres the Indian subcontinent has completed its journey north to plough into Asia, giving rise to the Himalayan mountains. The geography of the Earth is now quite like today's pattern of continents and oceans. Finally, in the last 40 metres you enter the Quaternary period, when the Earth cools rapidly and enters a new ice age – a series of long periods of glacial cold interrupted by short periods of comparative warmth, known as interglacials.

Ever since the last mass extinction 65 million years ago, the diversity of life has been increasing and is now richer than ever before. There is not the space to describe this diversity, so this final paragraph focuses on the emergence of one species. With 150 metres to go, early members of the *hominidae* appear, the family to which humans belong. The human species, *Homo sapiens*, emerges in Africa about 200 000 years before the present, just four metres from the finishing line. The final footstep covers approximately the last 11 000 years, known as the Holocene. It takes in the latest interglacial of the current ice age, during which human agriculture, nations and cities developed. But the impact of humanity's presence, the new human footprint, is beginning to have a major effect on the Earth. Some say this is so significant that we are changing the processes of deep time: that this signals the start of a new division of a new geological time, the *Anthropocene*, from the Greek *anthropos*, meaning human being.

Summary of Section 2

Section 2 has explored two timelines in deep time. In the longer first timeline, early life develops in the oceans and eventually helps create an oxygen-rich atmosphere. In the second, the development and expansion of life, biodiversity, is punctuated periodically by mass extinctions and significant global environmental change, including climate change. Throughout this long history, once life has developed in the oceans, it has hung on; in fact it has become richer in spite of major setbacks. The two constants have been the presence of the oceans, and a climate which, although it has varied considerably, has remained within limits suitable for life.

On the timescale of deep time, humans appear on the scene at the very last moment, but we are already changing the planet to a significant extent. Through our actions we are affecting biodiversity and changing the atmosphere and oceans. The next section moves from the Earth's past to its present to explore some of the reasons for this change.

Climate change and the carbon connection

3

The Earth is now getting warmer. According to the 2007 report from the *Intergovernmental Panel on Climate Change* (IPCC, 2007a), eleven out of twelve of the most recent years (1995–2006) were the warmest observed on Earth since long-term temperature measurements began in 1850. This is not an isolated set of figures, but the result of a long-term trend of warming, particularly in the last 50 years. Many regions of the Earth are now experiencing changes to climate and weather, including heatwaves, droughts and floods. These observations and events have led the IPCC to state:

> Warming of the climate system is unequivocal, as is now evident from observations of increases in global average air and ocean temperatures, widespread melting of snow and ice, and rising global average sea level
>
> *(IPCC, 2007a, p. 5)*

This section seeks to answer the question, 'Why is the Earth getting warmer?' At the end of the section a further question is raised: 'How significant are these changes for local and global environments?' The first question, and much of this section, has a narrow focus on causes. In the process of exploring them, this section introduces and discusses quite a few scientific terms and concepts. They are there as a guide for your understanding of the main argument, no more. The second question looks briefly at the wider consequences for our environment, a topic that will be returned to frequently in later blocks of the course. These are both big questions, which experts have difficulty answering. At the end of this section, if you can start to answer both questions to your own satisfaction, then you have made good use of this material.

3.1 Climate, weather, global warming and global climate change

First, some commonly used terms need introducing.

Temperatures vary widely over the Earth, from generally hot near the equator to cold near the poles, as do amounts of rain and snow. The weather experienced at any one place also varies from one day to another and between seasons. *Weather* refers to what is experienced at a particular time; for example it can be 'hot and sunny', or 'cold and windy'. *Climate* is the long-term average weather of a particular place, such as the temperature, rainfall and sunshine measured over many years, and includes a description of seasonal variations. A Mediterranean climate, for example, can be described as having a long, hot, dry summer; a cool, but not cold, winter; and a wetter autumn and spring. Climates have a major influence on the distribution of plants and ecosystems, but until recently were thought to be fairly stable. The difference can be summed up by the saying *'climate is what you expect, weather is what you get'*.

The basic measure of global warming is a rise in the average or **mean surface** temperature of the Earth. This mean value is usually quoted as 15 °C, but it has been getting warmer in recent years. It is defined as the air temperature measured by standard instruments close to the surface, when averaged over the whole planet, over both sea and land. For this reason it is generally referred to as the **global mean surface temperature**. Global warming and **global climate change** are often used interchangeably. Both refer to the changes brought about as a result of human activities altering the atmosphere, as opposed to **climate variability**, which refers to those due to natural causes that occur all the time. Here, use of the term global warming indicates a narrow focus and refers to a rise in the mean temperature of the Earth. The term global climate change, or just climate change, refers to changes affecting all aspects of climate, including, for example, changes in rainfall patterns as well as temperature, and is used to indicate a broader range of impacts on our environment. It could also mean that the temperatures fall instead of rise. The current long-term rising trend is not expected to change in the foreseeable future, however, although it might be interrupted over short periods and on a regional scale.

3.2 The third planet

Why does life exist on Earth but not its neighbours?

Figure 2.7 Earth from space

The Earth is the third planet from the Sun. Its orbit lies between that of Venus, which is closer to the Sun, and of Mars, which is further away. All three planets are composed largely of rock and metals, and have similar sizes, although Mars is smaller than the other two. In these two respects, they should all be capable of supporting life. The famous view of Earth from space, taken by the Apollo 17 astronauts in 1972, is reproduced in Figure 2.7. It shows a blue planet that is mostly covered by oceans and decorated with complex cloud patterns indicating our ever-changing weather. Mars and Venus, in contrast, are like barren deserts: there is no water on their surface and they are apparently lifeless. The Earth teems with life, but the other two planets do not. Why is there such a dramatic difference?

Section 2 highlighted the critical role played by oceans in supporting life on Earth. Life began in the oceans, and for much of the Earth's history existed only in the oceans. The presence of water, then, appears to be a requirement for life to survive and thrive, at least in the forms found on Earth. The history of the Earth also indicates that global temperatures, while varying considerably, have always stayed within a range suitable for life and to maintain oceans. Several of the mass extinctions noted in Section 2 have occurred when global temperatures were either very warm or very cold. What factors have helped maintain the Earth's mean temperature and make it habitable?

3.2.1 The Earth's mean temperature

The two main factors that influence the mean temperature of the Earth and its neighbouring planets are distance from the Sun and the nature and extent of their atmospheres. Consider first the situation if the Earth had no atmosphere.

The ultimate source of almost all the energy reaching the Earth's surface is the Sun. (Some heat energy flows from the interior of the Earth, but is tiny compared to the solar contribution.) The incoming energy is transmitted across space by solar radiation (the Sun's rays), and when it reaches the Earth is transferred to its surface, or to your skin which, as you will know from experience, warms. All bodies give off heat in the form of *infrared radiation*, at a rate that depends on their temperature. So the Earth, in turn, radiates energy back into space. Its surface temperature rises until the rate at which energy is transferred to it is balanced by the rate at which energy is radiated out to space from the surface of the Earth, as illustrated by Figure 2.8. Over time, if the output from the Sun is constant, the mean surface temperature of the Earth will stabilise at a particular value.

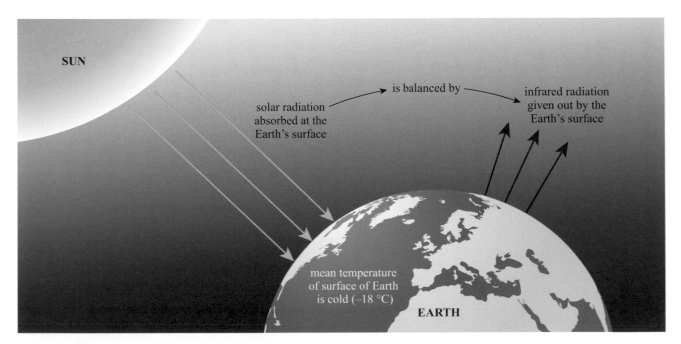

Figure 2.8 The energy balance at the Earth's surface, without an atmosphere. Solar radiation input balanced by infrared radiation from the Earth with a surface temperature of −18 °C.

At what temperature would it stabilise? If the Earth had no atmosphere, its surface temperature can be calculated to be approximately −18 °C (*minus eighteen degrees Celsius*). A similar calculation can be applied for our neighbouring planets: Venus, which is nearer to the Sun, should have a mean surface temperature of +50 °C, while for the more distant Mars the figure is −57 °C.

At this point you may have noticed the discrepancy between the calculation of −18 °C for the mean temperature of the Earth, and the value of +15 °C given at the start of the section. The difference between the two figures, +33 °C, represents a significant warming. This warming is the difference the atmosphere makes, and is known as the *greenhouse effect*. This is an entirely natural effect, which has existed as long as the Earth has had an atmosphere, although the value will have changed with the composition of the atmosphere. Note that we are not describing human impact here.

3.2.2 The greenhouse effect

How does the Earth's greenhouse effect work? The greater part of the Earth's atmosphere is in the lower atmosphere, and when dry it is made up almost entirely of three gases: nitrogen, with 78% (78 parts out of 100) by volume; oxygen (21%); and an inert gas, argon, most of the remainder. These three gases do not interact significantly with heat radiation from the Sun or the Earth. If these were the only gases in our atmosphere the Earth's mean temperature would remain at −18 °C. The two main naturally occurring greenhouse gases are *water vapour* and carbon dioxide. They are normally present only in small amounts, but their impact is very significant.

Greenhouse gases in the atmosphere are largely transparent to incoming solar radiation, but they intercept the outgoing infrared radiation from the Earth by absorbing it and then emitting it again in all directions. As Figure 2.9 illustrates, most energy radiating from the Earth's surface no longer escapes directly to space. Instead it is absorbed and re-radiated several times within the atmosphere. Some energy is sent back to the Earth's surface, some to the lower layers of the atmosphere; both are warmed. The radiation that escapes to space mostly comes from high in the atmosphere, where the temperature is much lower than at the surface. The Earth still radiates at an average temperature of −18 °C, so the theoretical balance still holds, but now the Earth is much warmer at the surface. The overall effect is for the atmosphere to act like the panes of glass in a greenhouse, keeping the Earth's surface much warmer than it would otherwise be.

Similar calculations apply to the quite different atmospheres of Mars and Venus. The measured mean temperature of the surface of Mars is −47 °C, compared to the estimate of −57 °C without an atmosphere. It has a much thinner atmosphere than the Earth: a barometer would record a pressure of less than one-hundredth that of Earth. However, because it is composed mostly of carbon dioxide its greenhouse effect is still significant at 10 °C,

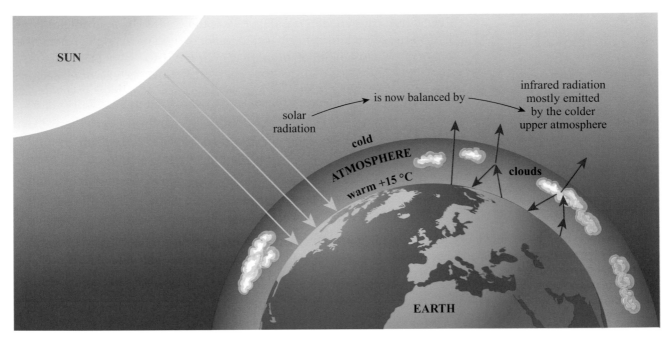

Figure 2.9 The 'natural' greenhouse effect of the Earth's atmosphere. The energy balance is maintained, but the surface of the Earth is at approximately 15 °C and the lower levels of the atmosphere are warmed.

though not enough to lift the planet from a deep freeze. Venus, by contrast, should have a temperature of +50 °C without its atmosphere, whereas its measured value is above 500 °C near the ground. Its surface glows with a dull red heat. Its predominantly carbon dioxide atmosphere has a pressure one hundred times greater than Earth, which is why the greenhouse effect is so large. Anyone unfortunate enough to land on its surface would be both crushed and fried!

At the start of this section we asked, Why does life exist on Earth but not, apparently, on our neighbouring planets? Part of the answer is that the Earth's distance from the Sun, in combination with the greenhouse effect of its atmosphere, maintains a range of temperatures on the planet that are suitable for oceans and life to survive. Mars, with its thin atmosphere and weak greenhouse effect, is too cold for life to flourish, while Venus, with its dense atmosphere and intense greenhouse effect, is too hot. The Earth is just right. This is sometimes referred to as the Goldilocks thesis, named after the children's story *Goldilocks and the Three Bears*, where Goldilocks finds the temperature for Baby Bear's porridge to be 'just right'. The good news (there sometimes is some) is that theoretical calculations suggest that we will not be able to pump enough carbon dioxide into the atmosphere to cause a runaway greenhouse effect like that on Venus. This is backed up by evidence from the Earth's history: the oceans and life have survived much higher levels of greenhouse gases than now, although life has often suffered setbacks including several episodes of mass extinction.

3.3 The carbon connection

Section 2 showed that the development of life on a dynamic Earth was associated with major changes in the composition of oceans and atmospheres, and that carbon-based life played a key role in this. The section above discussed how greenhouse gases in the atmosphere have a major effect on the mean temperature of the Earth, through the greenhouse effect. Once again, carbon in the form of carbon dioxide plays a major role. This section will explore more fully the role that the element carbon plays in the life of the planet by following two trails: first, the trail that carbon atoms follow as they cycle through different parts of the Earth, and then the carbon trail produced by human activity.

3.3.1 The first carbon trail, the carbon cycle

Carbon dioxide, CO_2, is produced and released into the atmosphere when we burn fuels, such as wood harvested from a forest, or coal and other *fossil fuels* extracted from the ground. It is also produced by almost all living things, both animals and plants, at all times of the day and night, in the process called *respiration*. In our own bodies we tend to equate respiration with the physical process of breathing, the movement of air in and out of our lungs. Within the lungs, oxygen from the air is taken in and some carbon dioxide is released from the body when we breathe out. When the oxygen reaches the cells of our bodies (and also the cells of other animals and plants), chemical reactions break down some of the complex carbon compounds such as *carbohydrates* that are stored in our bodies. This releases energy for our muscles to use. Oxygen is used in the process, and water and carbon dioxide are produced.

Fossil fuels, i.e. coal, oil and natural gas, are derived from fossilised organic matter (once living organisms)

What happens to the carbon dioxide? Section 2 described how plants and certain types of bacteria remove carbon dioxide from the ocean and atmosphere in a process called photosynthesis. This is the process whereby green plants, and a few other organisms, trap energy from sunlight and use carbon dioxide and water to make carbohydrates and oxygen. The carbohydrates are used to store energy for use in the growth and maintenance of the plant, and the oxygen is released to the atmosphere where it can be used again by plants and animals for respiration. The two processes of respiration and photosynthesis underpin the cycling of carbon, on which most life on Earth depends (Figure 2.10).

Figure 2.10 shows the fundamentals of the carbon cycle, but in this diagrammatic form it reveals little about the component parts of the cycle and the links between them. Figure 2.11 puts a little flesh on the bones. Animals are represented by a giraffe and plants are shown by a tree and some grass. The basic carbon cycle in Figure 2.10 can be traced in Figure 2.11 by arrows showing the movement of carbon dioxide. The respiration arrows from the tree and the giraffe to the air indicate production of CO_2, and the photosynthesis arrow shows CO_2 absorbed from the air by the tree. Both plants

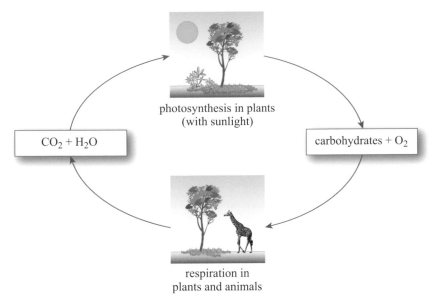

Figure 2.10 **The basic carbon cycle**

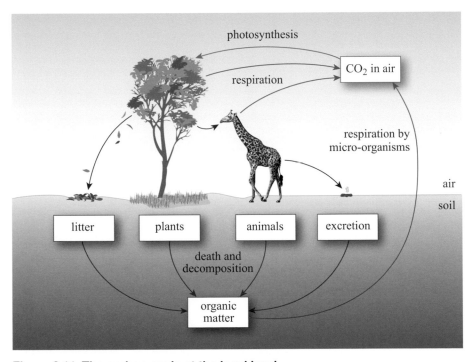

Figure 2.11 The carbon cycle at the local level

and animals contain carbon in their tissues in the form of carbohydrates and other carbon-based compounds known collectively as *organic* compounds. In Figure 2.11 the arrow from the tree to the giraffe makes the point that animals eat plants and that there is a transfer of carbon in the process.

So far, only the biological processes above the ground have been considered. Figure 2.11 also includes the vital parts of the cycle below the ground surface. While alive, both plants and animals produce waste products, for example in the form of *leaf litter* from trees and *excreta* from animals. These wastes and the remains of the dead plants and animals are broken down by *micro-organisms* living on and in the soil into simpler organic materials. In the process, these micro-organisms also respire and add carbon dioxide to the air. Any remaining organic matter will simply be incorporated into the soil.

Figure 2.12 represents the global carbon cycle and has been broadened to include interactions involving the oceans, aspects of the Earth's geology, and human activity. The discussion of this figure takes each of these components in turn.

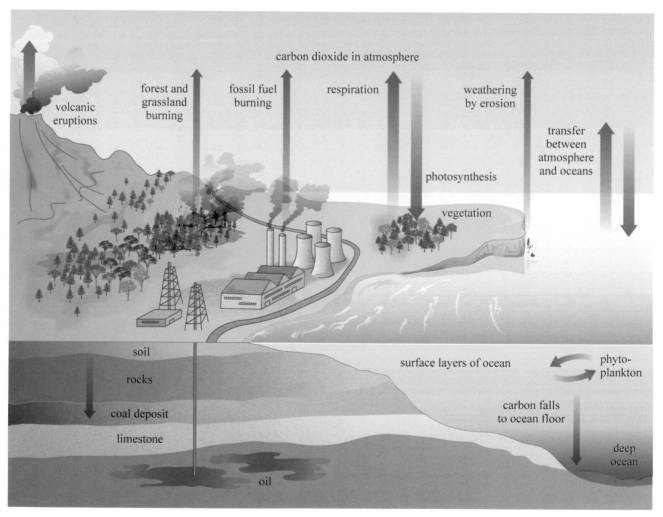

Figure 2.12 The global carbon cycle

In the oceans, *phytoplankton* (microscopic floating plants) play the same role as land plants in Figure 2.11. Carbon dioxide from the air dissolves readily in the surface waters and is used by phytoplankton in photosynthesis. However, as with green plants on the land, phytoplankton respire, so most of the carbon dioxide is returned to the atmosphere again from the surface of the oceans. Arrows show the two-way flows of carbon dioxide between the atmosphere and the ocean. Most of this activity takes place in the top few hundred metres of the ocean, the upper layer through which sunlight can penetrate and that is stirred by waves. Phytoplankton are eaten by *zooplankton* (microscopic floating animals), and both are eaten in turn by other marine animals. Many aspects of the carbon cycle shown for plants and animals on land are replicated in the ocean, although the details are not shown here. In addition, however, there is a slow trickle of carbon to the bottom of the oceans in the form of the dead remains of plankton and other marine organisms. Some of it remains in the ocean sediments, which eventually form new rock. Thus it is effectively removed from the main carbon cycle and enters what could be called the geological carbon cycle.

In Figure 2.12, two arrows point to geological mechanisms that remove carbon dioxide from the atmosphere. They indicate the slow processes of rock formation beneath the continents and the oceans, by which organic carbon is incorporated into rock strata, some in the form of coal, oil or gas, or mineral carbon from marine shells that forms rocks such as limestone and chalk (which are composed mainly of calcium carbonate). Other arrows show the return of this buried carbon as carbon dioxide to the atmosphere, through volcanic eruptions and weathering of rocks by erosion.

Two components of the global carbon cycle have now been identified: the biological carbon cycle, involving life on land and in the sea that continually exchanges carbon with the atmosphere, and a geological component that incorporates carbon in rocks before it is released to the atmosphere.

Where is most of the carbon on the planet? It lies buried in rock formations as limestone or chalk, or as organic deposits. Only one part in a thousand is found in *all* the other carbon stores, and 90% of that is dissolved in the deep oceans of the world where it does not mix readily with the upper layers. But as explained in the section on deep time, geological mechanisms function very slowly and it normally takes millions or even hundreds of millions of years for carbon buried as rock to emerge into the air again. Even the carbon in the deep ocean is very slow to mix with the upper ocean and it may be a thousand years before it reaches the surface again. For this reason, although these stores are massive, the amount of carbon they exchange with the air each year is tiny compared with the non-geological component. Most of the movement of carbon takes place between four main stores: the atmosphere, living animals and plants, soils, and the upper ocean. All four contain similar amounts of stored carbon.

What is the impact of human activity on the carbon cycle?

SAQ 2.2   Human activity and the carbon cycle

1   Identify from Figure 2.12 the sources of carbon dioxide in the atmosphere that arise from human activity.

2   Identify from Figures 2.11 and 2.12 the two stores that take up carbon dioxide from the air and the processes they use.

Study note: making notes

When you have finished reading a section or part, it can be useful to take time to check whether you have understood the main points. This is also an opportunity to go back over some of the relevant sections and make some notes. The purpose of making notes is twofold: to check that you have identified the main points from a section and to check your own understanding. Extracting the main points from a piece of writing and then writing them as notes in your own words is the best way of making sure that you have understood. An effective method of making notes is to start by 'skim' reading (a quick glance through to get an overview and some idea of the main points) and then rereading the material more thoroughly, highlighting (using a highlighter) the main points as you go along. Using these highlighted notes, you can then summarise by making a list using some of your own words.

3.3.2 The second carbon trail, human influences

Industrial economies, first in Europe and North America and now globally, have made increasing demands on the Earth to meet their material needs. We meet increasing demands upon agriculture to feed a growing and more affluent population by bringing more land under cultivation and using it more intensively. We are also heavily reliant on the use of the energy stored in fossil fuels to provide the electricity, heating and lighting and transport that modern societies take for granted. As a by-product of meeting these needs, we are inadvertently changing our atmosphere.

The global carbon cycle can help explain what happens when these activities release additional carbon dioxide into the atmosphere. The two main sources have been identified in SAQ 2.2. The first is the burning of fossil fuels, such as coal, oil and gas. These are compounds composed largely of carbon and hydrogen. When they are burned to release energy, carbon combines with oxygen to produce carbon dioxide (CO_2) and hydrogen combines with oxygen to produce water, (H_2O), usually in the form of steam. This process parallels the respiration by plants and animals illustrated in Figure 2.10. (Cement making, which uses limestone or chalk, also produces carbon dioxide and makes a lesser but still significant contribution.) The second is land use change for agriculture and the spread of urban areas, which includes the burning of forests and grasslands and also the release of carbon from newly disturbed soil. Recent estimates (IPCC, 2007a) suggest that fossil fuel burning is adding approximately 7 billion tonnes of carbon (sometimes referred to as gigatonnes of carbon, or GtC) to the atmosphere every year, with land use change contributing approximately 1.6 billion tonnes. Between 55% and 60% of these carbon releases, or emissions, remain in the atmosphere. The remainder is absorbed by the two carbon stores discussed in SAQ 2.2, namely by plants (mainly forests of the northern hemisphere) and the oceans.

Box 2.3   Describing large and small numbers (and units)

Why is seven billion tonnes sometimes written as:

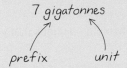

The term giga and its symbol G (note that some symbols are capitalised and some are not) is an example of an internationally agreed set of terms to describe numbers and units. These form the Système Internationale (international system) known as SI. The SI unit of length, for example, is the metre (m) and the SI unit for time is second (s). Here the prefix names, which come before the unit, are shown.

Example: What is one thousand metres in SI form? The prefix for one 'thousand' is 'kilo', so the answer is one kilometre (1 km in shortened form). One thousand metres, one kilometre and 1 km are alternative ways of describing the same thing.

There are several other different ways of writing large and small numbers, including fractions, decimals and powers of ten, which are shown here for reference.

Prefix	Prefix name	Meaning	Number and fraction	Decimal	Power of ten
G	giga	billion or thousand million	1000 000 000	1000 000 000	10^9
M	mega	million	1000 000	1000 000	10^6
k	kilo	thousand	1000	1000	10^3
		one	1	1	10^0
m	milli	thousandth	1/1000	0.001	10^{-3}
μ	micro	millionth	1/1000 000	0.000 001	10^{-6}
n	nano	billionth	1/1000 000 000	0.000 000 001	10^{-9}

Part 1 introduced the story of the Keeling Curve – the monitoring of the steady rise of carbon dioxide in the atmosphere – as an early sign of global environmental change. The discussion of the carbon cycle provides a mechanism, an explanation of why carbon dioxide is rising.

Figure 2.13(a) reproduces the Keeling Curve from Part 1, this time with an additional smoothed curve showing the predicted trend of carbon dioxide present in the atmosphere using estimates of global carbon emissions to the atmosphere. Figure 2.13(b) shows the smoothed curve adjusted to show 57% of the predicted emissions remaining in the atmosphere. There is now a good fit between the predicted trend and the measurements from the Mauna Loa Observatory.

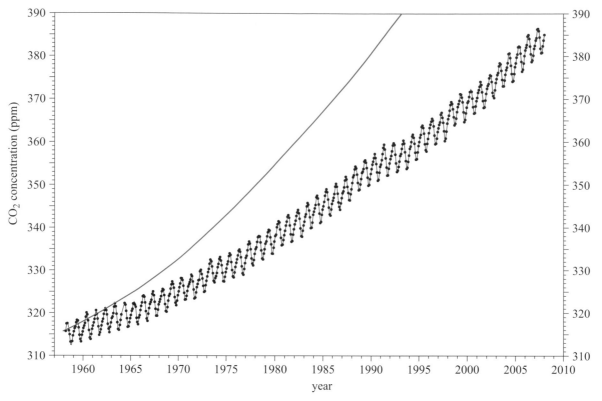

Figure 2.13(a) The Keeling Curve with trend line expected from CO_2 emissions *(Source: Keeling R., 2007)*

SAQ 2.3   Why is carbon dioxide rising in the atmosphere?

Why is the concentration of carbon dioxide in the atmosphere rising? Make notes from the explanation given in this section, in the form of bullet points.

How significant are these changes? Fossil fuels were deposited over periods of millions of years in the geological past. Industrial societies have only been in existence for a few hundred years and many countries have joined the industrial club more recently. During this time they have been extracting and burning these fossil fuels at an ever-increasing rate. The extent to which this is changing the atmosphere can be put in context by Figure 2.14, which shows concentrations of carbon dioxide in the atmosphere over the last 2000 years. For most of this period, the concentration of carbon dioxide remained close to 280 ppm; then, in the 1800s, carbon dioxide concentration started to rise, first slowly then rapidly, as fossil fuel use by industrialised countries increased.

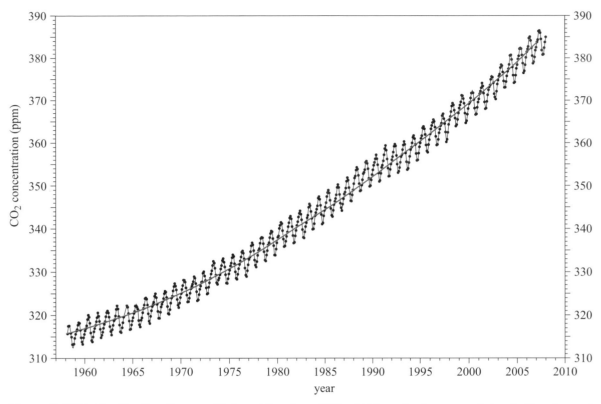

Figure 2.13(b) The Keeling Curve with trend line from 57% of CO_2 emissions remaining in the atmosphere
(Source: Keeling R., 2007)

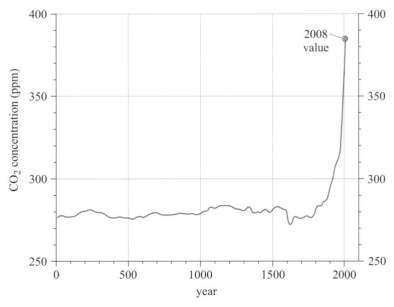

Figure 2.14 Concentration of carbon dioxide over the last 2000 years.
(Source: adapted from IPCC, 2007c, FAQ 2.1)

Figure 2.15 extends the timescale to 400 000 years ago. It shows graphs of global temperature and carbon dioxide concentration in the atmosphere, taken from an ice core in the Antarctic. Scientists extract this information from the air bubbles trapped in the ice core and can determine carbon dioxide concentrations accurately by this method. At first sight the two graphs look extremely complicated, which is not surprising as they chart the advance and retreat of the four most recent glacial periods on the Earth over the last 400 000 years. Figure 2.15(b) shows the change in the Earth's mean temperature from today's value. It shows that for most of this period the Earth experienced glacial conditions, with temperatures as much as 6–9 °C below those of today. These cold conditions were interrupted by briefer interglacial periods when temperatures were as warm as or warmer than today. The last glacial period ended some time between 10 000 and 20 000 years ago, and the period of comparatively warm and stable climate we experience now, known as the Holocene, is the latest interglacial. Block 2 discusses glacial periods and how scientists have unravelled the secrets locked in the ice.

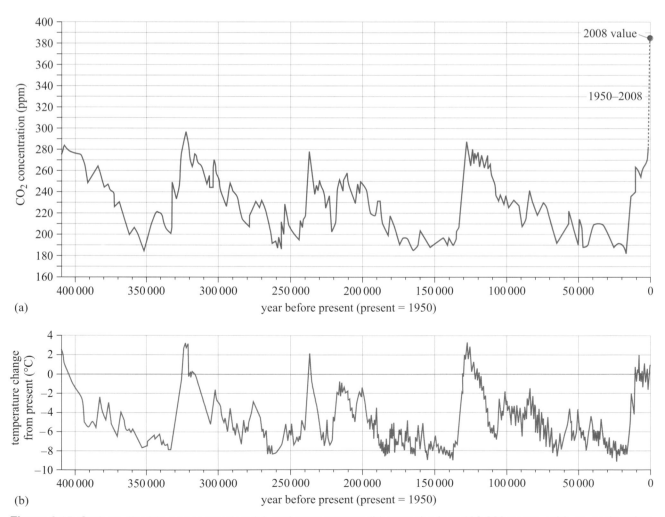

Figure 2.15 Carbon dioxide concentration (a) and temperature (b) over the last 400 000 years, with an estimation of concentrations in 1950–2008 (*Source: adapted from Petit et al., 1999*)

Figure 2.15(a) shows the carbon dioxide concentration in the atmosphere. The first point you may have noticed is the similarity between the two graphs. The jagged patterns track each other, illustrating that carbon dioxide concentration and global temperature are closely linked: they rise and fall together. The point to draw to your attention here is that throughout this time period carbon dioxide concentrations have fluctuated within a narrow range of 180–300 ppm. Recently, ice core analysis has extended the record back to 800 000 years and found that carbon dioxide concentrations and temperatures have remained in the same range. The level has mostly been below the 280 ppm measured over the last 2000 years – the time of human changes.

On the far right-hand side of Figure 2.15(a) is the 2008 value of carbon dioxide concentration, just above 385 ppm and rising every year. This demonstrates that carbon dioxide concentrations in the atmosphere are higher now than they have been for at least 800 000 years Now, refer back to the timeline of visible life in Table 2.3 and you will see that the first appearance of early humans is given as approximately 200 000 years ago. Although there is uncertainty about when precisely humans, *Homo sapiens*, first appeared, the timing corresponds approximately to halfway along the timescale of Figure 2.15. The current value of carbon dioxide is now the highest it has been since humans first walked the Earth, and humanity has achieved this change to our atmosphere in a mere two hundred years!

This is the end of the carbon trail. It has shown that human disturbance of the carbon cycle through fossil fuel burning and land use change is leading to concentrations of carbon dioxide in the atmosphere not seen since humans first appeared on the Earth. Is it possible to reverse these changes to our atmosphere? Figure 2.15 shows that rises in carbon dioxide concentrations do fall back again, but these occur over timescales of many thousands of years, whereas global climate change is happening now. One reason why scientists are so concerned about what is happening is that once carbon dioxide is in the atmosphere it is likely to stay there for more than a century. Even if carbon emissions stopped tomorrow, we are already committed to any changes resulting from our changed atmosphere for several generations.

SAQ 2.4   The effect of rising carbon dioxide

The concentration of carbon dioxide in the atmosphere has been rising significantly for many decades (see Figures 2.13 and 2.14). What effect would you expect this to have on the Earth's mean temperature?

3.4 Causes for concern

The increased greenhouse effect due to human activity is called the *enhanced greenhouse effect* (sometimes called the *anthropogenic greenhouse effect*) to distinguish it from the natural effect discussed earlier. The effect on the Earth is very much as though the output of the energy from the Sun has increased. As mentioned at the start of this section, the rise in the mean temperature of the Earth that occurs as a result is what is usually referred to as global warming.

Other greenhouse gases contribute to the enhanced greenhouse effect, in addition to carbon dioxide. The main two are *methane*, CH_4, and *nitrous oxide*, N_2O.

- Methane arises mainly from waste decomposition and as a by-product of certain forms of agriculture, including wet rice cultivation and cattle digesting food (belches).
- Nitrous oxide comes from decomposition of nitrogen-based fertilisers and industrial processes.

In the last few hundred years, their concentration in the atmosphere has increased: methane has more than doubled, while nitrous oxide has increased by a fifth. In both cases the trend has been similar to that of carbon dioxide, shown in Figure 2.14 – a long period when concentrations stayed close to a constant level, followed by a sharp rise about 200 years ago.

Further active materials released into the atmosphere as a result of human activity include two further groups of greenhouse gases:

- *ozone* in the lower atmosphere from burning of fossil fuels, e.g. from cars
- *chlorofluorocarbons* (CFCs) and similar compounds used in refrigeration, although these are being phased out
- *aerosols* or tiny particles in the atmosphere that can cause cooling as well as warming. A major source is sulphur dioxide from burning of coal in power stations, and oil.

*When water evaporates into the air it behaves as a gas. The phrase 'water vapour' refers to this gas, which is invisible, although we are aware of it because its presence determines the humidity of the air. Water vapour does not refer to mist or clouds

Finally, a few words about water vapour* are needed. Section 3.2.2 referred to water vapour as a naturally occurring greenhouse gas. It is not usually counted in the greenhouse gas ledger of the enhanced greenhouse effect because it behaves differently from other gases. Its concentration essentially responds to the temperatures of the surfaces from which it evaporates, and changes rapidly in time and place with the weather. Its main effect is thus to amplify the warming produced by other greenhouse gases, which is how it is predicted to behave by climate change models.

Should we be concerned about a warmer Earth? A Swedish chemist, Svante Arrhenius, was one of the first scientists to discuss the enhanced greenhouse effect. In 1904, he speculated that:

> "the slight percentage of carbonic acid [carbon dioxide] in the atmosphere may, by the advances of industry, be changed to a noticeable degree in the course of a few centuries". He eventually made the suggestion that an increase in atmospheric carbon dioxide due to the burning of fossil fuels could be beneficial, making the Earth's climates "more equable", stimulating plant growth, and providing more food for a larger population.

> *(NASA, n.d.)*

A little warming might seem a pleasant proposition to someone such as Arrhenius living in a cold climate near the Arctic Circle, but a hundred years on we have become aware that the changes may not be so positive.

As Figures 2.14 and 2.15 illustrate, the extent of the changes to our atmosphere and the rate at which they are changing are now thought to be unprecedented. Global warming in response to these changes has only just begun. Climate models predict that this century the Earth will warm significantly and at a faster rate than has occurred for millions of years – anywhere between 1 °C and 6 °C globally, depending on future emissions levels of greenhouse gases (IPCC, 2007a). Weather and climate are usually discussed in terms of the atmospheric elements of temperature, wind and rain. All regions of the world can expect to experience higher temperatures, changing patterns of rainfall – some drier, some wetter – and changing landscapes. But the climate system involves more than the atmosphere: it interacts with oceans, ice caps, and all living systems, including human societies. As global temperatures rise, the range and severity of possible impacts on physical and living systems are likely to increase. There is also concern that once global warming passes certain temperature thresholds, irreversible changes could take place. For example, the Greenland ice cap could melt, leading eventually to a sea-level rise of seven metres. Figure 2.16 gives examples of the impacts associated with each 1 °C of global warming. The figure should be treated with some caution, because there is always some uncertainty about the level of warming associated with the onset of a given impact, and this is not shown. Nor does the figure make allowance for any attempts to adapt to the worst effects. Nevertheless, the uncertainty is about when these impacts begin, not if they will.

Activity 2.2   Climate change impacts

From the information shown in Figure 2.16, make notes on the impacts of global temperature rises on:

1   effects on coastal regions for a rise of more than 1 °C

2   any new impacts occurring when a threshold of 3 °C is crossed.

Discussion

Figure 2.16 suggests that, within an unknown range of uncertainty, the impacts of rising global temperatures are:

1   Coasts

- above 2 °C millions *more* each year are affected by coastal flooding

- above 3 °C 30% of global coastal wetlands disappear

- above 4 °C sea-level rise threatens major world cities.

2   New impacts at 3 °C

- 30% of global coastal wetlands disappear

- increasing risk of abrupt, large-scale events, such as the loss of the West Antarctic Ice Sheet

- *significant* extinctions around the globe (significant is not explained in the figure, but the sources quoted mean 40% or more, rising with higher global temperatures).

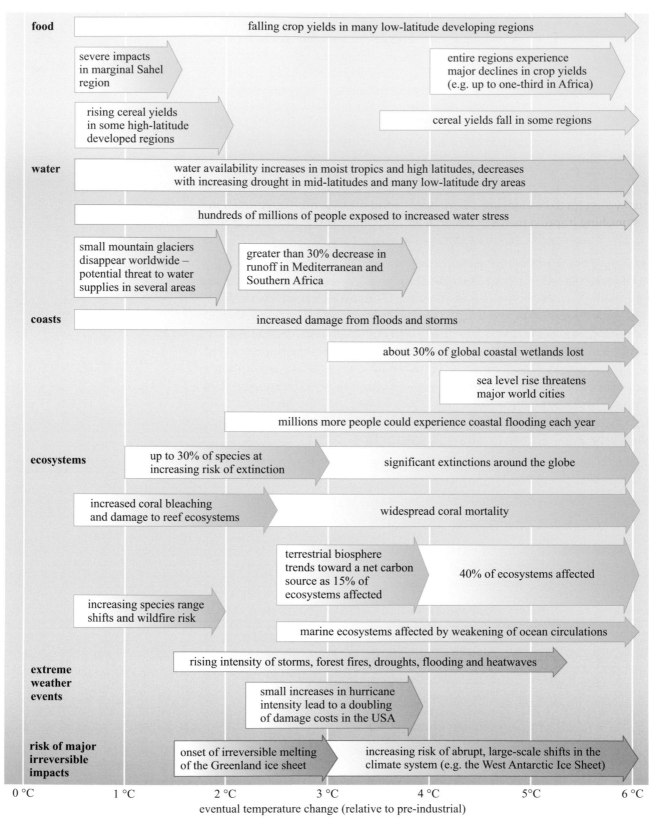

Figure 2.16 Climate change impacts associated with rising global temperature. The increase in shading for each impact indicates a rising level of risk *(Sources: adapted from HM Treasury, 2006, 'Summary', Figure 2; IPCC, 2007b, Figure 3.6)*

Sustainability – buzzword or byword?

4

Sections 2 and 3 have introduced some of the scientific work that has helped us to understand environmental change, and humanity's role in such processes of change. The effects of economic development since the Industrial Revolution are felt in the loss of biological diversity and habitats, and in local and global pollution and anthropogenic climate change. For most of those lucky enough to be enjoying a developed world lifestyle this has resulted in astonishing improvements in material wealth, choice and availability of food and consumer goods, freedom to travel, healthcare and life expectancy.

However, by the early 1980s the downsides of the transformations to humanity that were taking place became impossible to ignore. There were efforts to generate a new way of thinking about human progress that acknowledged that the economy, the environment and society all depend on each other. Their fates are inextricably bound up together, and one cannot be sustained without integrating the other two elements in considering any action. This is the thinking behind the concept of sustainability, or *sustainable development*. The integration of economy, environment and society can be illustrated as three interlocking circles (Figure 2.17).

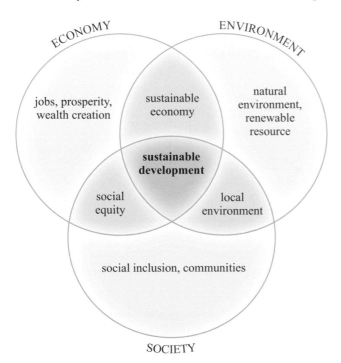

Figure 2.17 Sustainable development is based on the successful integration of economy, society and environment

The most concrete expression of the impact of sustainable development thinking on politics is found in the work of two decades of international policy meetings, described in Box 2.4.

Box 2.4   Sustainable development – a timeline of international talks

1980 World Conservation Strategy (WCS): environment ministers from around the world signed up to a commitment to pursue 'sustainable development'. The strategy was primarily driven by a concern with the conservation of habitats and species, and these issues came to be summarised by the term 'biodiversity loss'. The WCS is thought to be the first time the term is used in the context of an international political dialogue.

1987 The World Commission on Environment and Development (WCED, 1987), also known as the Brundtland Commission after its chair, the Norwegian Prime Minister Gro Harlem Brundtland, brought together leading international political figures to consider how to respond to the developing world's demands for economic advancement and the (mostly developed world's) concern for environmental protection. The 'Brundtland definition' of sustainable development was coined to try to square this circle. It stated that:

> sustainable development is development that meets the needs of the present without compromising the ability of future generations to meet their own needs.

(WCED, 1987)

This was a masterful piece of diplomacy that allowed all the key players to accept one (very flexible!) idea of the key characteristics of future development.

1992 United Nations Conference on Environment and Development (UNCED), also known as the 'Earth Summit', was held in Rio de Janeiro with world leaders in attendance. The meeting sketched out agreements and plans for further talks on key global environmental change issues, including climate change, biodiversity loss and forests. However, conflicting views of future development remained at the core of the debates, with leaders of the developed world intent on protecting their economies and electorates' lifestyles. At the same time many leaders of the developing world continued to insist on the right to develop economically, and environmentalists the world over argued that the agreements are 'too little and too late'.

The 2002 World Summit on Sustainable Development in Johannesburg confirmed that ten years on from the Rio Earth Summit the term sustainability still served as a very big umbrella for a wide range of opinion to gather under, but offered little in the way of concrete guidance. Environmentalists criticised the fact that businesses and government were happy to borrow the language of sustainability without acting on its principles.

By sifting through all of these talks and looking at initiatives at every level of human activity, from local to international, from voluntary to business, it is possible to identify some common features in definitions of sustainability. These include acceptance of:

- responsibility by present generations to address the interests of future generations
- limits to the Earth's capacity to absorb emissions, pollutants and wastes, affecting its ability to support human life
- limits to the supply of non-renewable natural resources
- the need for novel partnerships that ensure that economic, social and environmental interests are represented
- fairer distribution of resources, opportunities and responsibilities for action both locally and globally
- the need for near-term action leading to longer-term change.

These broad principles leave plenty of room for interpretation. The word 'sustainable' has been added to labels on everything from coffee jars to international meetings of heads of state in recent years (Figure 2.19). Supporters of the concept of sustainable development insist that its strength lies in precisely this adaptability. It has allowed leading figures from politics and business to engage with the idea of ecological limits on human activity. These are ideas that they might otherwise have dismissed as 'eco-babble'. These leaders have engaged with the ways in which their decisions (and lack of decisions in some areas) impact on issues such as biodiversity loss, deforestation and climate change in ways that a few years ago would have been unimaginable.

Nevertheless, the concept of sustainability is contested. Critics argue that the concrete achievements of the international talking shops appear very limited when compared with the scale of the problems they claim to address. Some go further, to suggest that the very term sustainable development is a dangerous distraction. They suggest that it is not physically possible to have

Figure 2.18 Gro Harlem Brundtland, Norway's former Prime Minister, who led the 1987 World Commission on Environment and Development

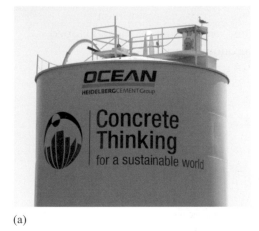

(a)

(b)

(c)

Figure 2.19 Conflicting images of sustainability. (a) and (c) hint at how businesses have learnt to deploy environmentalist language and imagery without necessarily changing behaviour; (b) shows campaigning cyclists promoting a very different vision of sustainability in a city.

endless economic development – the finite nature of the Earth's bounded system will simply not allow it. Rather, these critics argue that we should stop and think about what sustainability might mean in the here and now. Some environmentalists fear that 'greenwash', or tokenistic use of environment-related images and phrases, will do more to disguise the perilous state of the world than it will to deliver meaningful action.

Increasing numbers of senior business figures insist that their future lies in sustainable thinking, and sustainability has become a buzzword at international meetings. At the same time, environmental activists try to attract attention to their view of sustainability amidst tides of what they see as 'greenwash'.

Activity 2.3   Illustrating sustainability

How would you illustrate the terms *sustainability* or *sustainable development?* Imagine you are choosing a photo or other image for a Web-published essay on the subject. Suggest one or two images that can capture the thinking behind the terms as well as – perhaps better than – the terms themselves.

Discussion

If you search for images on the internet, for example at the big picture agency websites, using these terms you are presented with dozens of photos of electricity-generating windmills taken from every angle, plus a few solar panels, and some photos of international meetings (see also the examples in Figure 1.1 of Part 1). They say a picture is worth a thousand words, but in this case it seems difficult to summarise the issue in a picture or two. When I tried this exercise one image stood out: that of boats in Bangladesh equipped with solar panels (Figure 2.20). They move about a region where road access is very limited, and supply communities with recharging facilities for household electricity needs as well as a floating school with internet connections and healthcare. The schools are particularly important in raising levels of female literacy. Displacing kerosene lamps, the solar-charged lamps save money but also improve air quality (and health) in the home. The lamps are also used by night-fishermen, allowing them to earn more and work in greater safety. The non-governmental organisation (NGO) Shidulai seems to pack all the complex dimensions of sustainable development onto one boat.

Figure 2.20 One of the Bangladeshi non-governmental organisation Shidulai's boats that bring education, health and economic opportunity to otherwise isolated communities – an encapsulation of the concept of sustainability?

SAQ 2.5   Defining sustainable development

What is the Brundtland definition of sustainable development and when was it coined? What were the three global environmental change issues that were most prominent at the 1992 UNCED?

Sustainability is an immediately attractive notion, but it is an idea painted with a very broad brush. It is easier to get to grips with what sustainability means by looking at practical actions. Much of the change needed to make progress towards a more sustainable society needs to happen in the everyday choices made by ordinary people, particularly those living developed-world lifestyles. Part 3 introduces you to tools that can help to achieve this, specifically through the notion of your own carbon footprint.

Summary of Part 2

Section 1 introduced ways of thinking about the world in ecological terms. Section 2 then explored the history of the Earth from formation to the present day, including interactions between its oceans, atmosphere and evolving life. Section 3 went on to examine the role of greenhouse gases, particularly carbon dioxide, in maintaining a climate suitable for life. It described carbon flows through different parts of the Earth and raised the issue of global climate change caused by humanity altering these carbon flows. The final section discussed the concept of sustainability and sustainable development.

After completing Part 2 you should:

- be aware of the changes that have occurred on Earth over time due to natural and human influences
- appreciate the connection between carbon and climate change
- understand the complexities of the concept of sustainability
- have developed further reading skills and some note-making skills.

Answers to SAQs

SAQ 2.1

1 The early appearance of bacteria is recorded in a rock formation known as chert, which has been dated to 3600 million years ago.

2 Stromatolites are given as evidence of the existence of blue-green algae, which undergo photosynthesis.

3 The replacement of green banded-iron formations by red iron-bearing rocks is given as evidence of oxygen in the atmosphere that has also been taken up by the oceans.

4 The presence of tillites in the geological record is evidence of past glaciations.

SAQ 2.2

1 Sources of carbon dioxide from human activity, shown in Figure 2.12, are the extraction and burning of fossil fuel by industry (you might have added other uses, such as in homes and for transport), and burning forest and grasslands. Although fires occur naturally all year round, the use of fire to clear forest and grasslands, for example for agriculture, is a major source of carbon dioxide.

2 There are two stores that remove carbon dioxide from the air. The first store consists of plants, such as trees and grass on land, shown in Figure 2.11, and phytoplankton in the oceans, shown in Figure 2.12. The second store is the water in the upper ocean. Plants remove carbon dioxide by photosynthesis; the ocean dissolves carbon dioxide from the air.

SAQ 2.3

- Human activities have altered the global carbon cycle.
- Burning fossil fuels and changing land use emit significant quantities of carbon dioxide into the atmosphere.
- Just over half of the carbon dioxide emitted remains in the atmosphere.
- This has led to the steady rise of its concentration in the atmosphere recorded by the Keeling Curve.

SAQ 2.4

A rise in carbon dioxide concentration in the atmosphere will increase the existing greenhouse effect. This can be expected to lead to a rise in the mean surface temperature of the Earth.

SAQ 2.5

Gro Harlem Brundtland gave her name to a 1987 report that coined the most widely used definition: 'sustainable development is development that meets the needs of the present without compromising the ability of future generations to meet their own needs.' The three global environmental change issues that dominated the 1992 UNCED were climate change, biodiversity loss and forests.

References

Carson, R. (1962) *Silent Spring*, London, Penguin Books, reprint 1991.

HM Treasury (2006) *Stern Review: The Economics of Climate Change*, London, HM Treasury, http://www.hm-treasury.gov.uk/stern_review_climate_change.htm (Accessed 23 October 2008).

IPCC (2007a) Summary for Policymakers. In *Climate Change 2007: The Physical Science Basis*, Working Group I contribution to the Fourth Assessment Report of the Intergovernmental Panel on Climate Change, Cambridge, Cambridge University Press.

IPCC (2007b) *Climate Change 2007*: Synthesis Report of the Fourth Assessment Report of the Intergovernmental Panel on Climate Change, Cambridge, Cambridge University Press.

IPCC (2007c) Chapter 2. In *Climate Change 2007: The Physical Science Basis*, Contribution of Working Group I contribution to the Fourth Assessment Report of the Intergovernmental Panel on Climate Change, Cambridge, Cambridge University Press.

Keeling, R. (2007) *Lessons from Mauna Loa: On the value of continuous time series*, Ralph Keeling Presentations, Scripps CO_2 Program, http://scrippsco2.ucsd.edu/talks/rfk_hawaii_mlo_50th.pdf (Accessed 11 August 2008).

Lawton, J. H. (2001) 'Earth system science', *Science*, vol. 292, no. 5524, p. 1965.

Lovelock, J. (1992) *The Evolving Gaia Theory*, Paper presented at the United Nations University, Tokyo, Japan, 25 September.

NASA (n.d.) *On the Shoulders of Giants*, Earth Observatory Library, http://earthobservatory.nasa.gov/Library/Giants/Arrhenius/arrhenius_3.html (Accessed 6 August 2008).

Petit, J. R., Jouzel, J., Raynaud, D., Barkov, N. I., Barnola, J.-M., Basile, I., Bender, M., Chappellaz, J., Davisk, M., Delaygue, G., Delmotte, M., Kotlyakov, V. M., Legrand, M., Lipenkov, V. Y., Lorius, C., Pépin, L., Ritz, C., Saltzmank, E. and Stievenard, M. (1999) 'Climate and atmospheric history of the past 420,000 years from the Vostok ice core, Antarctica', *Nature*, vol. 399, no. 6735, pp. 429–36.

Scotese, C. R. (2008) PALEOMAP Project, http://www.scotese.com/earth.htm (Accessed 12 August 2008).

Stanley, S. M. (2005) *Earth System History*, 2nd edition, New York, W.H. Freeman and Company.

Tickell, Sir C. (2006) *Earth Systems Science: Are We Pushing Gaia Too Hard?* 46th Annual Bennett Lecture, University of Leicester.

Turney, J. (2003) *Lovelock & Gaia: Signs of Life*, Cambridge, Icon Books.

WCED (1987) *Our Common Future*, Oxford, Oxford University Press.

Zweig, P. (1981) 'Rhapsodist of deep time', *New York Times*, 17 May.

Part 3
Treading lightly on the Earth

Robin Roy

Introduction

1

This part aims to give you an understanding of the nature and importance of the *carbon footprint* of individuals and households, which is the annual amount of carbon dioxide and other greenhouse gas emissions they produce. It will enable you to assess your own carbon footprint and explore what you could do to reduce that footprint, and so 'tread more lightly on the Earth'. You'll learn what individuals and households can, and can't, do in order to help tackle harmful environmental change, and especially climate change.

In Part 2 you learned how almost all scientists agree that carbon dioxide (CO_2) released into the atmosphere largely from fossil fuel burning, together with emissions of other greenhouse gases, is rapidly changing the Earth's climate. Part 2 noted that these fossil fuels (coal, oil and natural gas deposits formed hundreds of millions of years ago) are being used at an increasing rate – starting with the Industrial Revolution about 200 years ago, but rising rapidly since 1945 – to provide all the goods and services the world's population now consumes. Fossil fuels formed in geological 'deep time' are being burned within a just few human lifetimes. Oil and gas in particular are being consumed faster – especially as fuels for transport, heating and electricity generation – than can be supplied into the foreseeable future, at least at reasonable prices.

As well as fossil fuels, other *resources*, including raw materials, water and land, are also required to supply these goods and services. This gives rise to a variety of other environmental challenges, such as deforestation, water shortages and waste. But in this Part 3, I'll focus on the problem of greenhouse gas emissions, especially carbon dioxide, and explore what you can do to lighten those emissions to help reduce the rate of climate change. You will assess your 'carbon footprint' and see what actions you and, if relevant, other household members could take to lighten that footprint. You will also better understand which actions are more and less effective, and the scope and limits of what individuals can do at the personal and household level.

You'll explore the answers to questions such as:

- What is the carbon reduction effect of changing your eating habits, compared to driving fewer miles or flying less often?
- By how much would you need to reduce your carbon footprint to achieve an environmentally 'sustainable' level of emissions?

From what you've just read, you'll realise that this part is based on the view, held by most environmentalists and many governments, that something should be done to reduce the rate of climate change, and that individuals and households can contribute to that effort. But even if you don't

Figure 3.1 The greenhouse effect due to increasing concentrations of carbon dioxide and other greenhouse gases in the Earth's atmosphere

agree with that view, you'll learn much from studying this part. It will also introduce some of the issues surrounding carbon footprints, discussed further in Part 4 of this block, such as:

- What is the individual's role in reducing carbon footprints, or is it a problem for governments and business?
- Why should people in developed countries like Britain lighten their carbon footprints when greenhouse gas emissions from *developing countries* and *newly industrialised countries*, like India and China, are growing extremely rapidly, as they industrialise and their populations grow?

> There are activities in this part involving use of a computer-based carbon footprint calculator, viewing audio-visual material on the course DVD, and accessing the course website and the internet. So you'll have to allow sufficient time for these.

1.1 What is the carbon footprint and why is it important?

The carbon footprint is the annual amount of greenhouse gas emissions, mainly carbon dioxide, that result from the activities of an individual or a group of people, especially their use of energy and transport and consumption of goods and services. It's measured as the *mass*, in kilograms or tonnes per year, either of carbon dioxide (CO_2) emissions alone, or of the *carbon dioxide equivalent* (CO_2e) effect of other greenhouse gas emissions.

The carbon footprint can also be calculated for an event, such as a football match or music festival, or of providing a product, such as a computer or a bag of potato crisps.

The carbon footprint is an *environmental indicator*: a way of measuring impacts on the environment. There are many other environmental indicators that measure different impacts, such as water pollution, loss of biodiversity and depletion of mineral resources (Box 3.1). This part focuses on only this single measure of CO_2 and other greenhouse gas emissions, but you should be aware that the carbon footprint doesn't measure other impacts, except perhaps indirectly.

1.1.1 Carbon dioxide and other greenhouse gases

Carbon dioxide (CO_2) is used as the basis for the carbon footprint because, as you read in Part 2, it is by far the main contributor to the enhanced greenhouse effect from human activity (mainly burning fossil fuels, clearing forests and making cement). So, often only CO_2 is counted in the carbon footprint. However, for a more complete measure of the carbon footprint the other human-generated greenhouse gases are converted into a CO_2 equivalent (in kilograms or tonnes CO_2e) in terms of their global warming effect and added to the footprint.

Box 3.1   Carbon footprint and ecological footprint

Another widely used environmental indicator is the *ecological footprint*, which is a measure of a population's (household, city, nation, etc.) environmental impact based on the *area of land and sea* theoretically required to indefinitely support their lifestyle at a given level of technology.

The ecological footprint measures the area of land and sea required to produce the population's food and accommodate its roads, buildings, etc. as well as the forested area required to absorb the population's CO_2 emissions. So the ecological footprint measures the carbon footprint component of a population's environmental impact using land area. Sometimes 10% land area is added to the ecological footprint for biodiversity conservation. The ecological footprint is the indicator used to support the argument that about three planet Earths would be needed if everyone in the world tried to live the lifestyle of an average European, which is clearly unsustainable. You'll encounter the ecological footprint again in Part 4 of this block.

Part 2 noted that the two main non-CO_2 greenhouse gases associated with human activity are methane (CH_4, mainly from cattle belching, manure spreading, wet rice growing and decomposing waste) and nitrous oxide (N_2O, mainly from nitrogen fertilisers and industrial processes). One tonne of methane has the equivalent global warming potential of 21 tonnes of CO_2, while one tonne of nitrous oxide is equivalent to 310 tonnes of CO_2. But because the amounts of methane and nitrous oxide released are much smaller, their emissions together add about 15% to the UK's contribution, and about 25% globally, to the enhanced greenhouse effect. This means that other greenhouse gases should not be ignored when assessing a carbon footprint, at least of individuals or households, although to simplify calculations they often are.

In this part I'll use the total CO_2 equivalent effect of carbon dioxide plus other greenhouse gases whenever possible, but where only information on carbon dioxide is available, I'll have to use only CO_2 emissions when discussing carbon footprints.

1.1.2 The carbon footprint boundary

Depending on where you draw the boundary, the carbon footprint can apply to an individual person, a household, an organisation or event, a product, a city, region or country, or the whole world. I'll mainly be considering the footprints of individuals, *households* and the countries they occupy.

But even then the boundary needs to be defined carefully. Sometimes the carbon footprint is taken to mean the individual's or household's *direct*

CO_2 emissions, mainly from burning fossil fuels for home heating and car driving. But this leaves out the individual's or household's *indirect* CO_2 equivalent emissions arising from the production and distribution of the food, drink and other goods and services they consume, ranging from clothes to electronic products, banking and medical services, and even Open University courses (Figure 3.2).

Again depending on the boundary, these indirect emissions often include only the goods and services produced within the country where people live, but they may also include emissions from imports, for example the products that Britain imports from China. As you'll see, an individual's indirect carbon footprint is often heavier than the direct footprint, and so should not be ignored, although again to simplify calculations it often is.

Whichever measure you choose, the 'footprint' image is used to suggest an individual or group treading on or occupying the Earth. It implies that the Earth can't indefinitely support the lifestyle of that individual or group, and if they are to live sustainably they'll have to lighten their footprint.

1.2 Individual and household carbon footprints

In this part I'll be referring mainly to the carbon footprint arising directly and indirectly from the activities of individuals and households.

The carbon footprint of individuals and households is important because they are ultimately the main consumers of the energy, food and other goods and services that produce those emissions.

Look at Figures 3.3(a) and 3.3(b) – what do they show?

First, these are *pie charts* and show the percentage breakdown of total and individual annual *carbon* emissions from the UK economy in 2004/5.

Study note: pie charts

A pie chart shows different amounts as slices of a circular pie. The whole pie represents the total or 100% amount and so a pie chart is useful for displaying percentage breakdowns – see also Study note: *percentages* below.

Second, the emissions are expressed in tonnes of carbon rather than carbon dioxide. This is another way of expressing emissions of the main greenhouse gas using just the mass of the carbon (C) atom rather than the whole carbon dioxide (CO_2) molecule. Always check whether emissions are given in kilograms or tonnes of C or of CO_2 and convert if necessary (see Box 3.2). But, since the mass of carbon emissions is directly proportional to the mass of carbon dioxide emissions the *percentage* breakdown is the same whether you measure the carbon footprint using C or CO_2 (see Study note: *percentages*).

Figure 3.2 The footprint as a powerful image of treading on or occupying the Earth. The direct UK individual's carbon footprint arises from home energy use and personal transport and the indirect footprint mainly from producing and consuming foods, goods and services *(Source: based on Tesco, 2008, p. 7 and Carbon Trust, 2006, p. 19)*

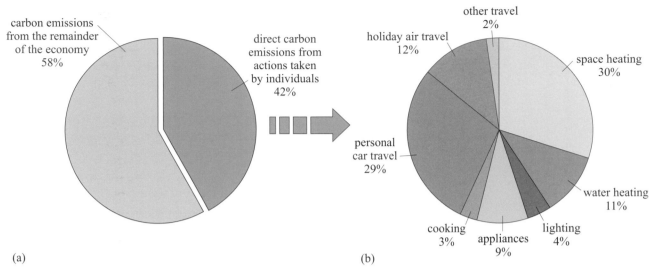

Figure 3.3 UK carbon emissions: (a) total *direct* and *indirect* carbon emissions from the UK economy. Total carbon emissions from the UK economy in 2004, including international aviation and shipping = 168.3 million tonnes carbon (MtC) per year, from NETCEN (National Environmental Technology Centre) data; **(b) breakdown of *direct* emissions by individuals.** Individual annual carbon emissions in 2005 = 1.16 tonnes carbon per person per year, from DEFRA data *(Source: DTI, 2007, p. 49)*

Box 3.2   Converting carbon to carbon dioxide emissions

1 tonne carbon emissions $= 1$ tonne $\times 44/12 = $ **3.67 tonnes CO_2** emissions

1 tonne CO_2 emissions $= 1$ tonne $\times 12/44 = $ **0.27 tonnes carbon** emissions.

Box 2.1 *The chemical elements* in Part 2 explained that this conversion arises because the mass of a carbon (C) atom = 12 units and the mass of an oxygen atom = 16 units, so the mass of a carbon dioxide (CO_2) molecule $= 12 + (2 \times 16) = 44$ units.

Third, the charts are based on carbon emissions alone and don't include the other greenhouse gases. So, as I mentioned in Section 1.1, the charts underestimate the total carbon footprint of the UK economy (in CO_2 equivalents) by about 15%.

Figure 3.3(a) shows that about two-fifths (42%) of total UK carbon emissions are the *direct* result of actions by individuals. Figure 3.3(b) shows how those direct carbon emissions from an average UK citizen break down in more detail.

As discussed earlier, there are different ways of graphically presenting numerical information. Figure 3.4 is a bar chart presenting the same information as in the pie chart in Figure 3.3(b). In this case you may find the bar chart (you met these in Part 1) clearer than the pie chart.

Looking at either Figure 3.3(b) or Figure 3.4 you can see that:

- space heating (i.e. heating rooms) plus water heating plus personal car travel, account for the biggest part of an average UK individual's direct carbon footprint (30% + 11% + 29% = 70% of the total)

- other important carbon footprints arise from running domestic appliances and lights (9% + 4% = 13%) and holiday air travel (12%)

- cooking and other travel (public transport and motorcycles) create relatively minor average individual carbon footprints (3% + 2% = 5%).

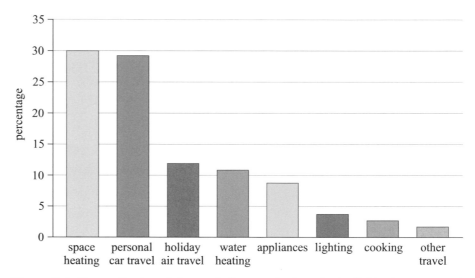

Figure 3.4 Alternative breakdown of *direct* emissions by individuals presented using a bar chart *(Source: HM Government, 2007, p. 26 (based on DEFRA, 2006))*

Now look again at Figure 3.3(a). It shows that the remaining 58% of total carbon emissions arise from the rest of the economy. This includes the *indirect* carbon footprint arising from individual and household consumption of food and other goods and services.

The other part of that 58% is those emissions not really associated with satisfying individual and household consumption, such as defence. This residue, which can't be allocated directly or indirectly to households, amounts to between a fifth and a quarter of total UK carbon emissions.

This means that individuals and households are directly or indirectly responsible for 75% to 80% of the UK's carbon footprint. This proportion is not unusual for an industrialised country where consumption of energy, food and other goods and services by households accounts for most economic output.

SAQ 3.1   The carbon footprint

(a) What is the carbon footprint?

(b) Give three different ways of measuring the carbon footprint (in terms of how the mass of emissions is calculated).

SAQ 3.2   Direct and indirect footprints

(a) Look at the caption for Figure 3.3(b). The average UK individual's direct *carbon* emissions are given as 1.16 tonnes per person per year. What is this mass expressed as *carbon dioxide* emissions?

(b) What are the two main components of the *direct* carbon footprint of individuals and households in developed countries with a climate similar to that of the UK?

(c) Give an example of an *indirect* component of an individual or household carbon footprint.

Study note: percentages

Percentages indicate proportions and show the number of parts out of 100. For example, 30% is 30 out of 100 and 65.2% is 65.2 out of 100.

You may need to use a calculator when working out percentages.

To change a percentage to a fraction, or to a decimal, the percentage is divided by 100. So for example, 30% expressed as a fraction is 30/100, or 0.3 expressed as a decimal; and 65.2% is 65.2/100 or 0.652.

To do the opposite, that is, to change a fraction or a decimal to a percentage, the fraction or decimal is multiplied by 100. For example, the decimal number 0.25 expressed as a percentage is $0.25 \times 100 = 25\%$. The fraction 41/50 expressed as a percentage is $41/50 \times 100 = 82\%$.

If you need to find out the percentage of something, convert the figures into a fraction and then multiply by 100. For example, if 42 people out of a group of 70 vote for a political party, the percentage voting for that party is 42 divided by 70 multiplied by 100, or $42/70 \times 100 = 60\%$.

You can also work out quantities from a percentage. Here are two examples.

(a) 20% of 350 people = $20/100 \times 350$ (or $0.2 = 350$) = 70 people.

(b) What is 350 kg of carbon dioxide emissions reduced by 20%? A 20% reduction on the whole 100% leaves $100\% - 20\% = 80\%$ of the whole. $80\% = 80/100$ or 0.8, therefore 350 kg reduced by 20% is $0.8 \times 350 = 280$ kg.

Summary of Section 1

The carbon footprint is the total mass of 'carbon' emissions that result from the annual activities of an individual or a group of people, from an event or from supplying a product. To be accurate, the carbon footprint should include the direct and indirect emissions of CO_2 and other greenhouse gases (mainly methane and nitrous oxide). However, for simplicity, carbon footprint calculations based on CO_2 or carbon emissions alone are often used.

Individuals and households are directly responsible for over 40% of the carbon footprint of developed countries and, including their indirect emissions, for 75% to 80% of the total carbon footprint. Hence lightening the carbon footprint arising from individual and household activities and consumption is very important in addressing climate change.

Not all footprints are equally heavy

2

At the end of this section you'll be asked to view some video material on the course DVD. But if you prefer, this can be left until the end of the next section.

You've just read some information about the carbon footprint of an average UK individual or household. But the actual footprint of any individual or household depends on the amounts and types of energy, food, and other goods and services they consume. This means that an individual's or household's carbon footprint depends on where they live, the type of dwelling they occupy, their age, income, job, *values*, personal circumstances and lifestyle. Thus, carbon footprints of different individuals and households vary widely within any given country, but also across different countries, and especially between rich developed countries (e.g. the UK), newly industrialised countries (e.g. China), and poor, developing countries (e.g. Uganda).

For individual or household carbon footprints, the *average* (or more correctly, the mean) footprint within a country is usually given (see Study note: *average and mean*). These averages show the variation in carbon footprints between different countries, but conceal the wide variation within each country.

Study note: average and mean

An average value is often used in order to get an idea of a 'typical' or expected value. There are different ways of expressing an average value but the most common is the *mean* (which is often referred to as the average, as I have here).

The average (or mean) is obtained by adding up all the values of a set of data and dividing by the number of items in the data set. For example, if three individuals have footprints of 13, 9 and 17 tonnes CO_2 per year, their total footprint is $13 + 9 + 17 = 39$ tonnes CO_2 per year. Their mean footprint is the total divided by the number of individuals $= 39/3 = 13$ tonnes CO_2 per person per year.

The mean is also used when several values contribute to an overall value, as in the case of assignment marks. If you have the following percentage marks for your assignments: 67, 82, 45, 75, 77, 68 you can work out your overall average (mean) score by adding the six scores together and dividing by the number of scores there are, i.e. $(67 + 82 + 45 + 75 + 77 + 68)/6 = 69$. (This assumes that the assignments are equally weighted.)

To calculate the mean carbon footprint of a UK citizen (in 2004) using the information in Figure 3.3(a), divide the total UK emissions of

168.3 million tonnes carbon by the UK population of 59.4 million. The result is 2.83 tonnes carbon per person per year.

To express 2.83 tonnes carbon as carbon dioxide emissions: $2.83 \times 44/12 = 10.4$ tonnes CO_2 per person per year (see Box 3.2 and Study note: *rounding numbers* at the end of this section if you're not clear how these calculations are done).

2.1 The carbon footprint of UK individuals and households

The simplest way of calculating the average (mean) carbon footprint of an individual living in the UK can be obtained by dividing total UK annual CO_2 emissions by the number of people in the country. Using the official government information in Figure 3.3(a), this produces a mean footprint of 10.4 tonnes CO_2 per person per year (as shown in the Study note: *average and mean*).

2.1.1 The effect of imports and exports

Recalling the importance of defining the carbon footprint boundary from the previous section, you may see a problem with this government foot-print calculation. This footprint doesn't include the CO_2 emissions pro-duced in other countries for the food, drink and other products imported into the UK. It also excludes the CO_2 emissions from goods and services produced in the UK for export.

A detailed study for the Carbon Trust (2006) took these imports and ex-ports into account. It gives an average UK carbon footprint of 11.3 tonnes of CO_2 per person per year, of which 0.9 tonnes arises from the CO_2 *embodied* in the food, products and services imported into the UK, minus exports. This means that the carbon footprint arising from UK emissions alone is: $11.3 - 0.9 = 10.4$ tonnes CO_2 per person per year (the same as the official figure given above). This study also provided a comprehensive breakdown of the carbon footprint of an average UK citizen (Figure 3.5).

2.1.2 Including other greenhouse gases

The above calculations count only carbon dioxide from fossil fuel use. But as you've seen, other greenhouse gases, especially methane and nitrous oxide converted into their CO_2 equivalents, should be included in the carbon footprint. This means that the above calculations underestimate the carbon footprint, especially of food supply, which generates large amounts of methane.

The most thorough attempt to include other greenhouse gases, as well as imports and exports, in the carbon footprint of UK households is a study for the Office for National Statistics. This provides a figure of 12.2 tonnes CO_2 equivalent per person per year in 2001 (Francis, 2004, pp. 8–9).

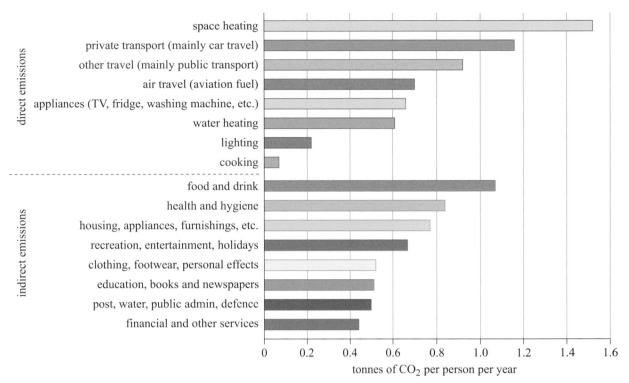

Figure 3.5 Breakdown of all the direct and indirect carbon dioxide emissions arising from the consumption of an average UK citizen, including imports and exports and government activities *(Source: based on data in Carbon Trust, 2006, pp. 19, 24)*

Of this total, just over a third (4.2 tonnes CO_2e per person) are *direct* emissions created by using fossil fuels for room and water heating, for powering lights and appliances, and for personal travel by car, public transport and aircraft.

A larger amount, about half of the total (6.2 tonnes per person), is generated *indirectly* by the CO_2e equivalent emissions involved in providing other goods and services at home and abroad. This includes the carbon dioxide and other greenhouse gases emitted when growing, harvesting, processing and distributing food, making and transporting consumer products, and running banks, schools and all the other services of a modern economy.

Finally, about 15% of the total (1.8 tonnes CO_2e per person) is for government activities such as defence, prisons, road building and other infrastructure that are not really a part of individual or household consumption.

The above figures are based on 2001 information. Using the latest available data, the carbon footprint of the average UK individual in 2005 was 12.3 tonnes CO_2e per person per year*, a small increase since 2001.

*In 2005 total UK greenhouse gas emissions were 733.5 million tonnes CO_2e (National Statistics, 2007, p. 25) and the UK's population was 59.6 million (DEFRA, 2007a)

SAQ 3.3   Carbon footprint reduction

If the UK carbon footprint in 1990 (a baseline date for calculating greenhouse gas reductions) was 13.4 tonnes CO_2e per person, and by 2005 it was 12.3 tonnes, what was the percentage reduction between 1990 and 2005? (See Study note: *percentages*.)

2.1.3 The effect of people and places

The footprints in the above Carbon Trust and National Statistics studies are for an average UK citizen. But footprints vary for different individuals and households. For example, another study showed that, on average, people aged 50 to 64 have heavier footprints than all other UK age groups, mainly due to their high spending on car and air travel, eating and drinking, and medical and financial services (Haq et al., 2007, p. 7).

The National Statistics study showed that the UK regions with the heaviest household carbon footprint were Northern Ireland (mainly due to above average use of oil and coal for heating) and the South-East (due to above average travel and goods and services consumption), and the lightest was Yorkshire and Humberside (due to below average footprints for travel and goods and services).

The carbon footprint per person varies with household size as well as region. One-person households generally have heavier footprints per person than those with two or more inhabitants, including children. This is because people living alone usually occupy and heat a bigger area per person and don't share most household goods and activities. For example, a one-person household in the South-East had *nearly three times* the carbon footprint per person of a Yorkshire household with three or more members (Francis, 2004, pp. 20, 27–28). So, one of the barriers to reducing carbon footprints is the growing number of one-person households (now nearly a third of all UK households). Sharing a household can be one of the most effective ways of lightening individual carbon footprints.

2.1.4 Identifying the carbon heavyweights

I've focused on two studies of the carbon footprint of UK individuals and households, but there are many others (e.g. WWF, 2006; Goodall, 2007 and Marshall, 2007a).

Despite these different calculations of the carbon footprint of UK individuals and households, they all result in *an average of about 10 to 11 tonnes CO_2 per person per year depending on whether imports and exports are included. If other greenhouse gases are included, the footprint is about 12 to 12.5 tonnes of CO_2 equivalent per person per year.* It means that you can be reasonably confident that these numbers are in the right 'ballpark'. However, the breakdown of emissions between categories varies in the different studies, mainly due to different ways of categorising the direct and indirect emissions.

Figure 3.6

Activity 3.1   The carbon heavyweights

(a) Look back at either Figure 3.3(b) or 3.4, and at Figure 3.5. What are the main sources of *direct* CO_2 emissions from an average UK citizen?

(b) Look again at Figure 3.5. What are the main sources of *indirect* CO_2 emissions from an average UK citizen?

Make a note of your answers before looking at the discussion below.

Discussion

The main individual direct CO_2 emissions are from:

space and water heating

transport (especially personal car travel and holiday air travel)*

home electricity use (for powering lights, appliances, electronics, etc.)

The main individual indirect CO_2 emissions are from:

food and drink (including agriculture, processing and distribution, catering, food imports and exports); the food footprint is actually heavier than shown in Figure 3.5 because methane emissions are not included.

use of services (insurance, finance, medical, recreation, hotels, education (e.g. Open University courses), water and telephone, etc.)

purchases of consumer goods (domestic appliances, clothes, shoes, furnishings, newspapers, etc.)

government activities (e.g. defence) and capital projects (e.g. road building).

*There is a difference between the two charts in the emissions arising from 'other travel'. This is probably due to different ways of categorising transport emissions.

The carbon heavyweights in other developed countries

The breakdown of individual and household emissions in most developed countries is similar to that for the UK. For example, the four main household sources of CO_2 and other greenhouse gas emissions across the European Union are: home energy use, food and drink consumption; personal travel; and tourism (European Environment Agency, 2005, pp. 7–10).

A US study (Brower and Leon, 1999, pp. 234–39) found that the breakdown of CO_2 and other greenhouse gases from American households was:

- 32% personal travel (mainly by car; air travel was about 2%)

- 30% home energy use (especially electricity for running lights and appliances, air conditioning and heating)

- 12% food and drink (especially production and consumption of meat and eating out)

- 12% consumer products (especially buying clothes, furnishings; cleaning products and paper goods)
- 6% housing (building and renting homes)
- 6% providing medical services (e.g. running hospitals, supplying medicines)
- 2% financial services (e.g. banking and insurance) and others.

This American study also showed that personal transport, food production and home energy use, as well as emitting large amounts of greenhouse gases, were also major sources of toxic air and water pollution and damage to wildlife habitats. These other environmental impacts are not included in the carbon footprint; this is something to remember when using it as an environmental indicator.

Although the breakdown of household emissions is similar for most developed countries, one difference is the amount of heating and cooling (e.g. ventilation, air conditioning) required in different climates. Figure 3.7 shows the energy demand for heating and cooling (modelled for very-low-energy houses) in cities in the UK, the USA and Spain. Similar low-energy houses in Beijing (North China) and in Hefei (mid-China) are included for comparison.

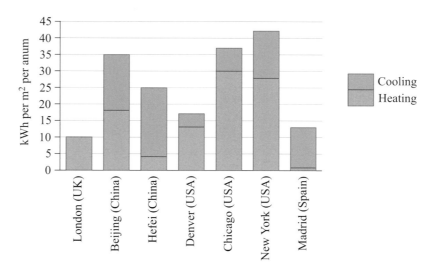

Figure 3.7 Energy demand for artificially heating and cooling homes in different climates. The heating and cooling demand is modelled in kilowatt-hours (kWh) of thermal energy per square metre per year of similar low-energy housing in order to make valid comparisons *(Source: Dunster et al., 2008, p. 127)*

If you look at the Figure 3.7 bar chart, you'll notice that no energy for cooling is required in the London house (although that is likely to change with global warming), whereas in Madrid, Spain, almost all the energy is for cooling, and there are different mixes of heating and cooling in the American and Chinese homes.

2.2 International comparisons of carbon footprints

You've seen that the carbon footprint of an individual or household is a simple idea, but calculating it can be quite complicated. It depends on whether you count only CO_2 or include other greenhouse gases; whether you count only the emissions generated within a country or include imports and exports; and whether you count emissions from government activities as part of a citizen's carbon footprint.

This means that international comparisons can be difficult and so are usually based on the simplest calculation, namely emissions of CO_2 within a country's borders. Hence different sources often give different footprints, depending on the statistics available, the year and the assumptions involved. You'll notice, for example, that the average carbon dioxide footprint within the UK quoted in this section varies, depending on the source and the year, from 9.2 up to 10.4 tonnes CO_2 per person – something you have to work with in a complex area such as emissions statistics.

2.2.1 Carbon footprints per person

Despite the simplifications and variations, the statistics clearly show the huge differences between countries in the carbon footprint of an average individual.

Activity 3.2   International comparisons

From looking at Table 3.1, what is the average UK carbon footprint (in tonnes CO_2 emissions per person per year) compared with the world average, and with average individual footprints in the USA, China, India, Sudan and Uganda?

Round your answer to one decimal place, or the nearest whole number, whichever seems most suitable (see Study note: *rounding numbers* at the end of this section.)

Table 3.1 Average CO_2 emissions for selected countries in 2004 (tonnes per person per year)										
USA	**Saudi Arabia**	**Russian Federation**	**UK**	**Greece**	**China**	**Brazil**	**India**	**Sudan**	**Uganda**	**World average**
20.4	13.9	10.5	9.8	8.7	3.8	1.8	1.2	0.3	0.065	4.0

Source: CDIAC, 2004

Here's an example. UK divided by Brazilian CO_2 emissions = 9.8/1.8 tonnes = 5.444444 = 5.44 to two decimal places, 5.4 to one decimal place and 5 to the nearest whole number. That is, an average UK individual's carbon footprint is over 5 times heavier than an average Brazilian's.

Spend no more than 15 minutes on this activity before looking at the discussion.

Discussion

An average UK individual's carbon footprint is:

about 2.5 times heavier than the world average

about 0.5 times (i.e. half) that of an average American

about 2.6 times heavier than that of an average Chinese

about 8 times heavier than that of an average Indian

about 33 times heavier than that of an average Sudanese

about 151 times heavier than that of an average Ugandan.

Figure 3.8(a) shows similar information presented more dramatically in graphical form for the year 2002. You can see that Luxembourg has an even higher carbon footprint per person than the USA. This is mainly due to its low population, high national income and its steel industry. In general, because wealthier people usually consume more and have more energy-intensive lifestyles than poorer people, they have heavier carbon footprints.

2.2.2 Total carbon footprints

Of course, the picture changes when you consider *total* CO_2 emissions for different countries rather than emissions per person. Figure 3.8(b) is another chart that shows that America was by far the greatest total emitter of CO_2 in 2002, but, owing to their huge populations, China and India were second and fifth (compared to 47th and 51st in emissions per person). The UK was the seventh largest source of CO_2 emissions in the world. As noted above, a country's carbon footprint is broadly related to the wealth of the population (see Figures 3.9(a) and (b)). But other factors also have an effect, such as whether the country has industries that use a lot of energy.

In 2007, with its rapid economic growth and building of new carbon-heavy coal-fired power stations, China was estimated to have overtaken the US as the world's largest source of CO_2. Together the USA and China emit over 40% of the world's CO_2, while India could become the world's largest emitter of CO_2 before 2020 (Cabinet Office, 2007, p. 12).

Figure 3.8 (a) Average carbon dioxide emissions per person (in tonnes CO_2 per year) for different countries as at 2002. Some Middle Eastern countries (e.g. Qatar) with very high and many African and Asian countries with low CO_2 emissions per person are not shown; **(b) average total carbon dioxide emissions (in million tonnes CO_2 per year) for different countries as at 2002. The CO_2 emissions for the year 2006 are about 12 to 15 per cent higher than the figures shown here.** Many African and Asian countries with low total CO_2 emissions are not shown. By 2007 China had probably overtaken the USA as the largest source of CO_2 emissions *(Source: Time for Change, n.d.)*

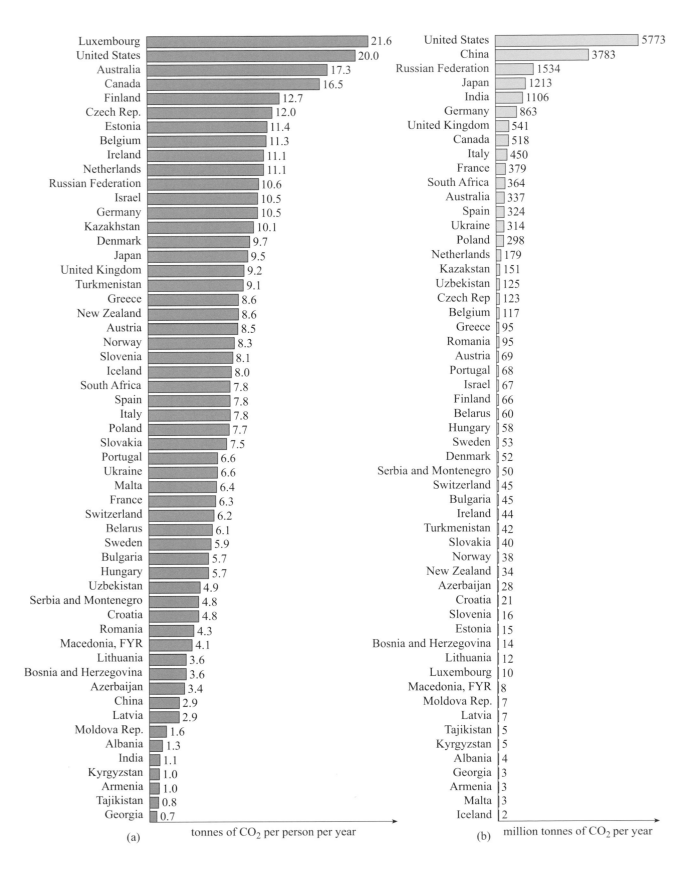

(a)   tonnes of CO_2 per person per year

(b)   million tonnes of CO_2 per year

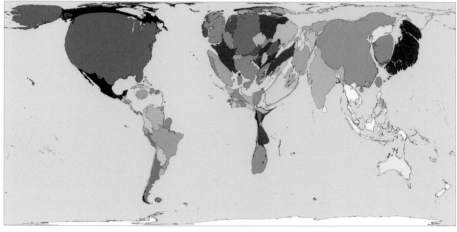

(a)

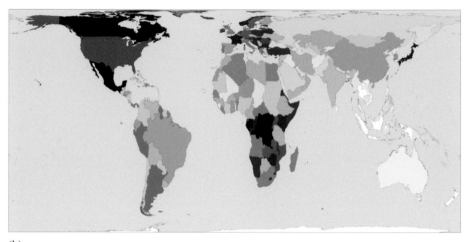

(b)

Figure 3.9: (a) world map with territory size distorted according to the proportion of greenhouse gas (GHG) emissions from that territory. The map of territory size according to the wealth of that area looks very similar, indicating the relationship between, and the global inequalities in, people's purchasing power and their country's GHG emissions (measured in tonnes of carbon dioxide equivalent); **(b) world territories map for comparison** *(Source: Worldmapper, 2008a and 2008b)*

2.2.3 Differences between people and places

I said at the beginning of this section that the average individual and household carbon footprints for a country conceal the differences within that country. These differences in carbon footprints are related to income and can be enormous, but difficult to quantify.

For example, in India the 2004 average carbon footprint of 1.2 tonnes CO_2 per person per year hides the differences between: middle-class Indian households living in air-conditioned apartments and owning a television, refrigerator and motor scooter, or perhaps a car (Figure 3.10(a)) and the household of a subsistence farmer, whose only fuel is dried cow dung for cooking, and perhaps kerosene for a lamp (Figure 3.10(b)).

Or in Africa, the contrast between the elite, who may have a private swimming pool, and villagers who have to collect water for cooking and washing (Figures 3.10(c) and (d)).

And in China, where the lifestyles of the wealthier members of the very rapidly growing urban population contrast with that of people living in China's villages and rural areas (Figures 3.10(e) and (f)).

(a)

(b)

(c)

(d)

(e)

(f)

Figure 3.10 (a) apartments, New Town, Kolkata, India, built for India's fast growing middle class; (b) Indian cattle farmer living on less than £1 per day; (c) government official's house, Libreville, Gabon; (d) villager's house, Jinja, Uganda; (e) typical apartment block, China; (f) village alley, near Yangshuo, China

Similar contrasts could also be shown between the homes and lifestyles of rich and poorer people in developed countries.

The Carbons and the Tans

So far, I've used the carbon footprint as an indicator of how heavily individuals and households are 'treading on the Earth' and affecting the climate. But it's still a rather abstract idea. The course DVD contains extracts from a 2006 BBC/OU TV programme *Can we save planet Earth?* that provide striking visual images of a household's carbon footprint – represented by black blocks of carbon coming out of a house or car. The programme examines the carbon emissions of a fictional average suburban family – the Carbons – who live in a rich developed country, rather like the USA. The programme contrasts the Carbons with an upwardly mobile couple – the Tans – about to move into a new apartment block in a suburb of a Chinese city, mainly fuelled by carbon-heavy electricity from China's coal-fired power stations.

I suggest that you now read the Study note: *viewing for a purpose* (below) then view the video introducing the Carbons and the Tans, which lasts about 9 minutes. This should get you thinking about the carbon footprint activity in the next section.

However, if you prefer, you could leave this material until the end of the next section and view it together with another extract about what the Carbons (and others) could do to reduce their carbon footprint.

When you've viewed the video, attempt SAQ 3.4.

Study note: viewing for a purpose

Throughout this course we have made available a variety of audio-visual and multimedia materials, including short pieces of video. Such video clips can be a very powerful medium for showing and explaining complex subjects. They can help you move away from static words to show the dynamics of events, interactions and processes.

To view video effectively, make sure you can watch without distractions, just as you would if you were trying to learn from text. Before you view any video material, spend a little time thinking about why you are watching it. Is it to help you gain deeper understanding of a topic in the block or to provide illustrative background material? Will you need to incorporate ideas from what you have seen into an assignment? To learn effectively from watching, read any notes supplied or the relevant sections of the course before you watch.

When you are watching you'll learn from the commentary, the opinions of people interviewed, and from the visual images – a great deal of information to take in at once.

After you have viewed a video, spend some time writing down the main points you picked up. Avoid trying to write down everything – key points that reflect the purpose of the piece will be most useful in triggering your memory and understanding. You may want to note down questions or links to things you have seen before.

You can, of course, stop viewing at any time to take notes or go through to the end – do what works best for you. Sometimes the material may be very rich, and you may feel it is worth viewing several times, but consider whether you have the study time to do this.

Where we have provided audio material, similar advice applies to learning from listening.

If you use these techniques to learn from the audio-visual material in this course, we hope that you will be able to use the many programmes on broadcast TV concerning environmental issues more effectively in order to enhance your knowledge and understanding. A word of caution – words and images on video and TV can be very engaging and may very easily convince you. They, however, give only a version of events and, as with written materials, you'll need to ask questions about the reasons behind the programme and whether alternative views of the world may be just as valid (remember the two articles about polar bears in Part 1).

SAQ 3.4   Interpreting The Carbons video

I'm assuming that you've read the Study note: viewing for a purpose.

(a) What does *The Carbons and the Tans* video say is the Carbons' household carbon footprint? (It includes only home energy and personal transport plus food.)

(b) What are the Carbons' CO_2 emissions per person per year (for home energy, transport and food)? Based on this footprint, in which country are the Carbons likely to be living?

(c) How do the Carbons compare to the average carbon footprint of individuals living in the UK (for home energy, transport and food, using information from Figure 3.5) and China (using information from the video)?

Study note: rounding numbers

Numbers are often 'rounded up' or 'rounded down' depending on how precise the numbers need to be. Often a good approximation of a number, particularly a large one, is adequate and this process is called 'rounding'.

When rounding a number up or down you need to look at the digit immediately to the right of the digit you are rounding to (up or down). If this right-hand figure is between 0 and 4 (i.e. less than 5), the digit you are rounding to stays the same, and if it is between 5 and 9 (i.e. 5 or greater) then it is raised to the next whole number. For example:

62 to the nearest 10 is 60, as the digit to the right of the 6 is 2, which is between 0 and 4 and so the 6 remains the same;

454 to the nearest 100 is 500, as the digit to the right of the 4 is 5, which is between 5 and 9 and so the 4 is rounded up to a 5;

1398 to the nearest 1000 is 1000, as the digit to the right of the 1 is 3, which is between 0 and 4 and so and the 1 remains the same;

29 321 to the nearest 10 000 is 30 000, as the digit to the right of the 2 is 9, which is between 5 and 9 and so the 2 is rounded up to a 3.

Decimal places

Decimal places and significant figures are two commonly used ways of showing the degree of precision.

Decimals are often rounded to a given number of decimal places. Decimal places are those to the right of the decimal point, e.g. 5.368 has three decimal places. To round this to two decimal places: find the second decimal (6) and look at the number to the right (8). As that number is between 5 and 9, the second decimal is rounded up to the next whole number, which is 7. So 5.368 rounded to two decimal places is 5.37.

To round 5.363 to two decimal places: the figure to the right of the second decimal place is less than 5, so it remains as it is. So, 5.363 rounded to two decimal places is 5.36.

Significant figures

If you are dealing with very large or very small numbers, rounding to a number of decimal places is not convenient. Instead you need a way of rounding numbers that just considers the most important digits in each number. These are called the most significant digits or figures and tell you roughly how big or how small the number is. The first significant figure in a number is the first *non-zero* digit on, or starting from, the left (ignoring the location of any decimal point).

For example, the first significant figure in 3 246 485 is the 3. It tells you that the number is between 3 and 4 million. The first significant figure in 0.000245 is 2, which tells you that the number is between 2 and 3 ten-thousandths. You can round a value off to any number of significant figures in a similar way to decimal places. Here are two examples:

(a) Rounding 3174 to 2 significant figures (the abbreviation of sig. fig. is often used).

The 1st sig. fig. is 3 and the 2nd is 1. The digit to the right of the 1 is 7; this is between 5 and 9, so the second significant figure is rounded up to 2, giving the answer: 3174 = 3200 (2 sig. figs.)

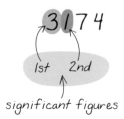

(b) Rounding 0.0446 to 1 sig. fig.

    The 1st sig. fig. is 4. The digit to the right is 4; this is between 0 and 4, so the 1st sig. fig. is rounded down to 4, giving the answer: 0.0446 = 0.04 (1 sig. fig.)

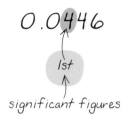

0.0**4**46

1st

significant figures

Summary of Section 2

The carbon footprints of individuals and households vary widely within countries and also between countries, related to people's incomes and life-styles and the country's industries. For example, the carbon footprint of an average Briton is eight times that of an average Indian, over 150 times that of an average Ugandan and half that of an average American.

The biggest components of an individual or household carbon footprint in developed countries arise from home energy use, personal travel, food consumption and purchase of goods and services.

Although there are different ways of calculating the total carbon footprint of UK individuals and households, they result in an average of about 10 to 11 tonnes CO_2 per person per year, or 12 to 12.5 tonnes of CO_2 equivalent per person per year.

3   How heavy is your footprint?

Most of this section involves using a computer for running a carbon calculator available on the course website. You'll also be viewing video material on the course DVD.

You've seen that individual and household carbon footprints vary widely both within and between countries. So, in this section you'll be working out your own carbon footprint using a computer-based calculator.

The calculator will show you which activities (energy use, travel, etc.) make large and small contributions to your carbon load.

But because the calculator is a *model* of reality, it can give you only an approximate measure of your carbon footprint and its components. Models are *simplified* representations of the real world, such as maps, architectural sketches, scale models and prototypes, that can help people to understand, visualise, experiment or make changes. In this case, the calculator is a model based on a set of mathematical equations that enables a computer to convert the information you enter into carbon emissions per person per year.

The results can only be as good as the accuracy of the assumptions and equations within the model and the information you enter into it. For example, if you drive a medium petrol-engine car, a calculator typically works out the carbon footprint of your car travel by multiplying the annual car miles (or kilometres) you enter into the calculator by the mean CO_2 emissions per kilometre for 1.4 to 2 litre petrol engines, divided by the number of people you say normally occupy the car. Or, if you don't know your annual car mileage, the calculator may ask about the number and length of car journeys you make and works out an approximate mileage from that. The reliability of the footprint depends on how accurate is the data you enter and how close your car emissions are to the average for 1.4 to 2 litre petrol engines.

Most carbon calculators also enable you to try out the effects on your footprint of making changes to your behaviour and/or the products and services you use – driving less or more, buying a car with a smaller or larger engine, saving heating energy and so on. This experimentation, without actually having to make any changes, is a form of *computer modelling*, but will normally give only approximate results.

Activity 3.3 Your carbon footprint

To calculate your carbon footprint, you'll need access to the carbon calculator and the notes for Activity 3.3 in the *Carbon Calculator Guidance Notes*.

Find the *Carbon Calculator Guidance Notes* (on the course website).

Find the carbon calculator on the course website and get it running. The *Guidance Notes* will help you to do this.

Read the *Guidance Notes* and use the calculator to work out your carbon footprint.

When you've completed Activity 3.3, keep a record of your individual carbon footprint and compare it with the average for the country where you live, using the information provided by the calculator and/or in Section 2 of this part.

The Carbons and Pacala's wedges

You may have already viewed the video The Carbons and the Tans *while studying Section 2. If you haven't, look back at the video notes and Study note:* viewing for a purpose *at the end of Section 2 and view that video now. Then view the second video* The Carbons and Pacala's wedges *about what the Carbons could do to lighten their carbon footprint.*

The two videos last about 9 and 11 minutes respectively, so together are about 20 minutes' viewing. The Carbons' footprint reduction strategies should help prepare you for Activity 3.5 Lightening your carbon load, in the next section.

Lightening household carbon footprints

The focus in the second video is on how to reduce household CO_2 and other greenhouse gas emissions from home energy use, food consumption, and personal car and air travel.

Global carbon stabilisation slices or wedges

The Carbons' attempts to reduce their footprint also introduces you to Steve Pacala, who with Robert Socolow created a 'slices', or wedges, model that describes national and international strategies for stabilising carbon dioxide emissions over the next 50 years. Their strategies are mainly technological, such as increasing the energy efficiency of buildings and increasing low-carbon sources of energy. The wedges model shown on the video is based on their 2004 calculations and aims only to *stabilise* global emissions. But *reductions* in these emissions will be necessary to stabilise *concentrations* of carbon dioxide and other greenhouse gases in the atmosphere, as was discussed in Part 2 and will be noted in the next section. Pacala and Socolow have since updated their work and increased the number of wedges to produce emissions reductions. You'll learn more about Pacala and Socolow's wedge model in Part 4 of this block.

After viewing, if you haven't already done so, attempt SAQ 3.4 at the end of Section 2, then SAQ 3.5.

SAQ 3.5

(a) What personal actions are recommended in the second Carbons video to lighten the carbon footprint of individuals and households in developed countries such as the UK and the USA, or at least to prevent household footprints getting heavier?

(b) From your experience of using a carbon calculator, which of these actions are likely to have the biggest effect? Is this a comprehensive set of actions?

(c) If everyone took these kinds of action, what effect would this have on Pacala and Socolow's carbon stabilisation wedges or slices?

Summary of Section 3

Individual and household carbon calculators are models that use mathematical equations and assumptions to convert information that you provide about your home, travel, etc. into an approximate figure for your carbon footprint.

Some computer-based calculators also allow you to quickly model the effects of making changes (e.g. to your home's energy efficiency or your travel behaviour) on your carbon footprint, and so work out the best ways of lightening it.

Lightening your carbon load

4

Most of this section requires you to continue using the carbon calculator.

If you've completed the carbon calculator Activity 3.3, you'll have a good idea of your carbon footprint and the relative contribution to the total load made by different components of consumption. You'll also know how your footprint compares to that of an average person in the UK.

If you live outside the UK, you may have used a calculator that provides somewhat different information about your carbon footprint.

Unless you already live a very 'green' lifestyle, it is unlikely that your carbon footprint will be light enough to be compatible with long-term environmental sustainability (a concept that was discussed in Part 2).

A sustainable carbon footprint is estimated to be 2 to 2.5 tonnes CO_2 equivalent per person, which is the annual amount if everyone on Earth produced an equal share of greenhouse gas emissions reduced by 50% to 60%, or the average UK carbon footprint of about 12.5 tonnes CO_2e per person was reduced by at least 80%. According to the authoritative Stern Review (HM Treasury, 2006), the scientific evidence shows that a 50% global reduction, and a 60% to 80% reduction in developed countries' greenhouse gas emissions is needed by 2050 to reduce the risk of the world suffering the most serious consequences of climate change. Importantly, Stern calculated that the cost of taking the actions to achieve these reductions will be much less than the costs of dealing with the storms, floods, food and water shortages, etc. of not doing so. Stern's arguments were subsequently reinforced by the fourth report of the world's main climate science advisory body, the Intergovernmental Panel on Climate Change (IPCC, 2007).

4.1 Carbon reduction targets

Let's now look at carbon footprint reduction targets in a bit more detail.

The first international agreement to set carbon reduction targets was the 1997 United Nations **Kyoto Protocol**, which requires developed countries to reduce their human-generated greenhouse gas emissions by an average of just over 5% on 1990 levels by 2008 to 2012. By the time the treaty came into force in 2005, only the USA and Australia had refused to sign*. The developing countries that did sign, including India and China, were not required to meet any reduction targets. The Kyoto Protocol was a very modest first step and is generally considered to be inadequate to meet the challenges of climate change, but the process of replacing it with a new international agreement is under way.

*A new Australian government finally signed the Kyoto Protocol in December 2007

Check the course website regularly for updates and reports on developments such as this.

Having signed up to the Kyoto Protocol, the UK government set itself more radical targets to reduce the nation's CO_2 emissions by 20% by 2010 and 60% by 2050. Although the 2010 CO_2 target is now unlikely to be achieved, the UK should do better than its Kyoto obligation to reduce its total greenhouse gas emissions by 12.5% between 2008 and 2012.

Box 3.3   Contraction and convergence

Current national and international targets for reducing greenhouse gas emissions, and especially CO_2, are increasingly based on a principle called *contraction and convergence*, developed by the Global Commons Institute, founded in 1990 by a former musician named Aubrey Meyer. The principle is that once a 'safe' concentration of CO_2 equivalent in the atmosphere is scientifically established, every country should 'contract' its emissions, aiming to 'converge' towards an equal share of emissions per person that avoids the long-term concentration rising above the safe level. The safe level is a matter of continuing analysis and debate, but has been interpreted as the concentration that gives about an even chance that the average global temperature will not rise by more than 2 °C (possibly up to 3 °C), at least in the long term. Some consequences of such increases in average global temperature are shown in Figure 2.16 in Part 2, Section 3. It means that while developed countries like the UK will have to drastically reduce their emissions per person, some developing countries would be allowed to increase theirs to the globally equal or 'fair share' level (Figure 3.11).

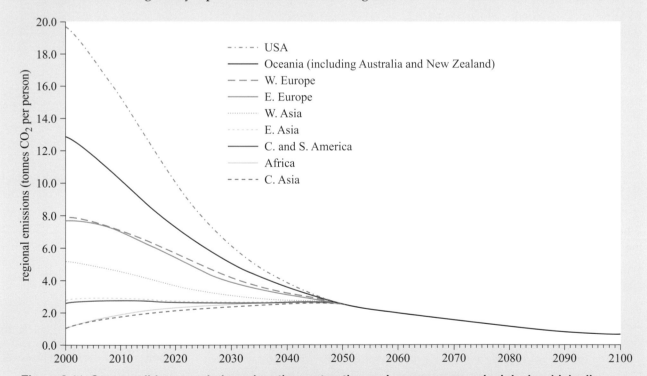

Figure 3.11 One possible scenario based on the contraction and convergence principle, in which all countries and regions of the world 'contract' their emissions to 'converge' on an equal share of 2.5 tonnes CO_2 emissions per person per year by 2050 *(Source: adapted from Dunster et al., 2008, p. 12)*

The contraction and convergence principle lies behind the UK government's Climate Change Bill (2008). This requires a legally binding reduction of at least 26% in the nation's CO_2 (and other targeted greenhouse gas emissions) by 2020 and at least 80% by 2050, compared to 1990 levels.

These are challenging targets, especially as they include international aviation and shipping. The Committee on Climate Change (2008), set up to advise on the targets, recommended bigger cuts of 34% to 42% in UK greenhouse gases by 2020 and supported the minimum 80% reduction by 2050, all on 1990 levels.

In parallel to the UK's target setting, in 2007/8 the European Union agreed a target of an overall 20% reduction in its 27 members' greenhouse gas emissions by 2020, or 30% if a new international agreement on greenhouse gas reductions were reached. Each country is also set individual 2020 targets that exclude greenhouse gas emissions from electricity generation and large industrial plants, which are dealt with separately; for example, the Danish reduction target is 20%, the UK's 16%, Germany's is 14%, while Poland can increase its emissions by 14% (CEC, 2008).

You can see that because of international politics and negotiations, and evolving climate science, there are many targets and timescales. You don't need to know all the details, except that the scientific consensus is that big reductions in greenhouse gas emissions, and especially CO_2, will be needed from most countries to avoid dangerous climate change. Equally important, for political acceptance by developing countries in Africa and newly industrialised countries like India and China, long-term emissions targets may have to be based on moving towards the contraction and convergence principle of global equal shares per person.

What might these targets mean for your carbon footprint?

Activity 3.4 Carbon footprint targets

If you live in the UK, in 1990 the average individual carbon footprint was about 10.5 tonnes CO_2 per person per year, or together with other greenhouse gases 13.4 tonnes CO_2 equivalent per person per year (Baggott et al., 2007, p. 10).

What would be the required carbon footprint for an average UK individual given the following targets?

(1) The UK government's original target of a 20% reduction in CO_2 on 1990 levels by 2010.

   What would this carbon footprint target be if other greenhouse gases were included, assuming they add approximately another 15% CO_2 equivalent emissions to the target?

(2) The 2008 Climate Change Bill target of at least a 26% reduction in greenhouse gas emissions by 2020 (assume a reduction of 40% on 1990 CO_2 equivalent emissions based on the Committee on Climate Change (2008) recommendations).

See Study note: *percentages* for help in working out percentage reductions.

(a)

(b)

Figure 3.12 (a) the average UK individual's CO₂e footprint of 12.5 tonnes; (b) the government's target of a reduction of at least 26% by 2020.

If you live outside the UK, find the CO_2 emissions per person for your country from Figure 3.8(a). Then work out your individual target footprints using the overall EU reduction targets of 20% and 30% by 2020. If your country is not listed, try searching the internet for 'CO_2 emissions per person' (or 'CO_2 emissions per capita').

Discussion

(1) By 2010 the average UK footprint should have fallen to 100% − 20% = 80% of the 1990 figure of 10.5 tonnes = 80/100 × 10.5 = *8.4 tonnes CO_2 per person per year.*

If other greenhouse gases are included, this would make the target approximately 15% higher at 8.4 × 1.15 = about 9.7 tonnes, *say 10 tonnes CO_2 equivalent per person per year* (but reduced from a higher starting point).

(2) By 2020 the average UK footprint should have fallen to 100% − 40% = 60% of the 1990 figure of 13.4 tonnes = 60/100 × 13.4 = *about 8.0 tonnes CO_2 equivalent per person per year.*

It's now time to start using the carbon calculator to explore how your carbon footprint might be reduced by amounts such as these. Remember that individual and household consumption is ultimately responsible for generating most of a country's greenhouse gas emissions. Also bear in mind that at the time of writing (2008) the UK's target is a reduction in greenhouse gas emissions of at least 80% by 2050.

Activity 3.5   Lightening your carbon load

For this Activity you'll need access to the carbon calculator and *Carbon Calculator Guidance Notes.* You should have already obtained these materials for Activity 3.3 *Your carbon footprint.*

Read the *Guidance Notes* for Activity 3.5 and use the calculator to work out how to lighten your carbon footprint to the targets given in the *Guidance Notes.*

4.2 Technical and behavioural actions

The numbers generated by the carbon calculator use a computer model based on some of the best information available. However, as I mentioned earlier, the results are not exact because calculators typically require you to enter broad categories of information about yourself and your household. And there are always uncertainties about some of the data on which the calculator is based. Nevertheless, the calculator allows you to explore the important actions needed to lighten your carbon load and discover which are likely to have large or small effects on your footprint.

You may have noticed that the actions fall into two broad groups – *technical* and *behavioural*. For example, installing low-energy lamps in your home is a 'technical' action, and switching off lights when leaving a room is a 'behavioural' action.

SAQ 3.6

Identify two technical and three behavioural actions included in a carbon calculator that should help to lighten your carbon footprint.

Summary of Section 4

There are many national and international targets for reducing greenhouse gas emissions, especially CO_2.

Increasingly these targets are based on emissions necessary to give a reasonable chance of the world avoiding dangerous climate change.

For reasons of political acceptability and equality, different countries are set different targets, which may be based on the principle of contraction and convergence.

A carbon footprint calculator is one way of exploring how to lighten individual or household carbon footprints by target amounts. However, it can provide only an approximate calculation of the effects of different technical and behavioural actions.

5   Treading lightly on the Earth

Nobody made a greater mistake than he who did nothing because he could only do little.

(Edmund Burke, 1729–1797)

At the end of this section you'll view two video case studies on the course DVD. You'll also need to access the course website.

If you want to consider how to further lighten your carbon footprint, you may need more detailed information on the effect of technical and behavioural actions not covered by the carbon calculator, or included only as a part of other actions.

5.1 Actions for lighter living

It's important to understand which actions are really worthwhile and which may hardly be worth worrying about. Tables 3.2 to 3.5 give a few examples of 'light living' actions for energy, transport, food, goods and services. But be aware that *the carbon emissions or savings from the actions listed in these tables depend on assumptions and approximations, and so should be seen as indications of relative impacts rather than exact numbers.*

Box 3.4   Coffins as a carbon footprint measure

Later in the course, you'll read about an architect (Peter Clegg) who had the idea that it's easier to visualise 1 kg of CO_2 by *volume* rather than by weight. He noted that 1 kg of CO_2 at atmospheric pressure occupies just over half a cubic metre. That's approximately the volume taken up by ourselves and the space immediately around us, or roughly the volume of a typical coffin, which he felt was a suitable image for climate change. So you could visualise the CO_2 emissions in Tables 3.2 to 3.5 in *'coffins-worth'*. For example, driving 9000 miles per year in an average car produces nearly 3000 coffins-worth of emissions, while installing loft insulation could save 300 to 1000 coffins-worth every year.

The effect of an action on your footprint will often depend on your own situation. For example, the annual CO_2 savings from installing loft insulation are calculated for an average three-bedroom UK house and vary according to the age of the house and how much insulation is already

Table 3.2 Carbon dioxide emissions savings – home energy

Home energy	Average saving (CO_2 per year)	28 tonnes CO_2e per year for an average three-bedroom UK house		Source
		Saving (per cent of average)	Notes	
Insulate solid walls (for UK homes built before about 1930)	2100 kg	7.5%	External or internal insulation, including 15% 'rebound effect'	DEFRA (2007b)
Insulate loft to 270 mm (10 in) thick	1000 kg to 300 kg	4% to 1%	Between no existing and 50 mm (2 in.) existing loft insulation	EST (2008a)
Replace old central heating boiler with an energy-efficient condensing model	875 kg	3%	'A' rated condensing boiler	EST (2008a)
Install cavity wall insulation (for UK homes built after about 1930)	625 kg	2%	Including 15% 'rebound effect'	DEFRA (2007b)
Lower room temperatures by 1 °C	300 kg	1%	Based on 10% reduction in energy use	DEFRA (2008), p. 9
Turn off standby on appliances, including power supply plugs	175 kg	0.7%	E.g. TV, audio, microwave, phone chargers computer, printer, etc.	DEFRA (2008), p. 14
Replace 5 × 60 W light bulbs with 11 W energy-saving CFLs (compact fluorescent lamps)	40 kg	0.2%	Average hours use. Replacing 100 W light bulb with 20 W CFL and/or higher use will produce larger savings	DEFRA (2007b)

Table 3.3 Carbon dioxide equivalent emissions savings – goods and services

Goods and services	Saving (CO_2e)	Average individual footprint is 12.5 tonnes CO_2e per person per year		Source
		Saving (per cent of average)	Notes	
Upgrade computer instead of replacing	220 kg per year	2%	(4-year life)	Hilty and Ruddy (2000), p. 6
Recycle 100 glass bottles	25 kg	0.2%	500 gram bottles; instead of landfill	WRAP (2006), p. 9
Recycle 100 aluminium cans	15 kg	0.1%	15 gram cans; instead of landfill	WRAP (2006), p. 13
Save 10 000 litres of water	10 kg	0.08%	20% average annual consumption per person; 1.0 grams per litre	EST (2008b)
Don't buy a new organic cotton top	2.4 kg	0.02%	Includes farming, raw materials, manufacture and distribution	Carbon Trust (2008)
Avoid using 100 plastic carrier bags	0.1 kg	0.001%		Ecobilan (2004), p. 38

Table 3.4 Carbon dioxide emissions – transport

Transport	Average emissions CO_2	Average individual footprint is 12.5 tonnes CO_2e per person per year		Source
		Saving (per cent of average)	Notes	
Annual UK car use 14 500 km (9000 miles)	4350 kg to 2200 kg	35% to 18%	Large petrol to small diesel car	DEFRA (2007c) p. 5
Annual 100 km (60 mile) per day car commuting	4500 kg	36%	Average petrol or diesel car 0.2 kg CO_2 per km; 225 days	DEFRA (2007c) p. 5
Annual 100 km (60 mile) per day rail commuting	1350 kg	11%	UK national rail 0.06 kg CO_2 per passenger km; 225 days	DEFRA (2007c) p. 12
100 × 8 km (5 mile) car trips	160 kg	1.3%	Average car = 0.2 kg CO_2 per km	DEFRA (2007c) p. 5
100 × 8 km (5 mile) bus trips	75 kg	0.6%	Average bus 0.09 kg CO_2 per passenger km	DEFRA (2007c) p. 15
100 × 8 km (5 mile) cycle trips	8 kg	0.06%	Based on additional food energy required	T263 (Block 2) p. 119
Long-haul international flight e.g. London to New York, USA return	2300 kg	18%	0.11 kg CO_2 per passenger km (× 1.9 for additional global warming effect) × 11 200 km	DEFRA (2008), p. 18, 36
Short-haul international flight e.g. Manchester to Barcelona, Spain return	333 kg	3%	0.10 kg CO_2 per passenger km (× 1.9 for additional global warming effect) × 1720 km	DEFRA (2008), p. 18, 36
UK domestic flight e.g. Glasgow to London return	380 kg	3.2%	0.18 kg CO_2 per passenger km (× 1.9 for additional global warming effect) × 1100 km	DEFRA (2008), p. 18, 36

Table 3.5 Carbon dioxide equivalent emissions – food choices

Food	Average CO_2 equivalent emissions	Average individual footprint is 12.5 tonnes CO_2e per person per year		Source
		Saving (per cent of average)	Notes and average consumption per year	
1 kg beef	15 to 32 kg	0.1% to 0.3%	Production (the main impact) 6.5 kg beef	Foster et al. (2006), p. 85; MAFF (2000)

1 kg chicken	4.5 to 5.4 kg	0.04%	Production (the main impact) 13 kg chicken	Foster et al. (2006), p. 93
1 kg cheese	8 kg	0.06%	6 kg cheese	Wallén et al. (2004), p. 528
1 kg rice	6.4 kg	0.05%	10 kg rice	Foster et al. (2006), p. 43
6 eggs	1.7 kg	0.01%	90 eggs	Foster et al. (2006), p. 107
1 litre milk	1.5 kg	0.01%	Mostly agriculture 35 litres milk	Foster et al. (2006), p. 68
1 kg loaf of bread	1.0 kg	0.01%	Production and consumption 37 kg bread	Foster et al. (2006)
1 kg potatoes	0.2 kg	0.002%	37 kg potatoes	Wallén et al. (2004), p. 528
waste less edible food	320 kg per year	2.5%	20% by weight of edible food is thrown away	WRAP (2008)

present. Actual savings also depend on the so-called *rebound effect*. This is the extent to which energy efficiency savings are reduced because people often heat better-insulated homes to higher temperatures, or spend the money they've saved on fuel bills on other things that produce CO_2 emissions. An allowance for the rebound effect of insulation measures is included in Table 3.2.

The emissions from car travel are well established: you can look up CO_2 emissions per kilometre of different models on official websites. But emissions from air travel can vary widely, depending on whether the additional effect on the upper atmosphere of the nitrogen oxides and water vapour in aircraft emissions is counted. The science is disputed and so in some carbon calculators, such as the official UK one, this effect is ignored, while in others the basic CO_2 emissions from a flight may be multiplied by up to three times. If a factor is used (as in Table 3.4), based on current science the government recommends multiplying CO_2 emissions from flights by 1.9 (DEFRA, 2008, p. 18). A voluntary *carbon offset* can be one way of reducing at least some of the carbon footprint of air travel or other activities; however, it is important to carefully check the nature of the offset scheme (see Box 3.5).

Box 3.5   Carbon offsets

Many airlines and other companies offer 'carbon offsets' as a way of reducing the carbon footprint of air travel or other activities. A voluntary carbon offset is a reduction in emissions, often resulting from a project undertaken in a developing country, sold to an individual or organisation to compensate for (offset) the carbon footprint arising from their activities.

"I drove to the garden centre for a tree to offset my carbon footprint...
so now I've got to go back for another one..."

Figure 3.13 © www.cartoonstock.com

However, the benefits of many carbon offset schemes are questionable, including those that involve tree planting, not least because it takes years for the trees to absorb CO_2 emissions from, for example, a flight made today. However, a scheme called the Gold Standard promises more worthwhile carbon offsets, as it approves only those which fund renewable energy and energy efficiency projects and promote sustainable development for the local community where they take place. In Britain, DEFRA is introducing a quality standard for carbon offset providers. But whatever the type of project, a carbon offset is a payment to transfer the responsibility for reducing emissions from the person or organisation creating the emissions to someone else.

The CO_2e savings from changing diets or recycling materials are also difficult to calculate exactly. Many of the figures given depend on complex life-cycle analysis studies (a concept you met in Part 1), the results of which can vary widely, depending on how the boundaries are defined and the assumptions used. For example, while it is clear that cows and sheep produce large amounts of the powerful greenhouse gas methane when digesting their food, the effects of reducing meat and dairy consumption depend on what is substituted. If out-of-season, imported vegetables and rice are substituted, the impact could be greater than for a diet with small amounts of locally produced, beef and lamb fed on grass rather than imported grains.

Also in Part 1 you looked at where some of your food comes from and were introduced to the idea of 'food miles'. Buying locally produced food to reduce those miles can help to save carbon, especially if it is imported by air. However, for most foods the main impacts arise from its production and processing, and reducing food miles may not always be the best option. For example, imported tomatoes grown outdoors in Spain have a lower carbon footprint than tomatoes grown in a heated greenhouse in the UK.

You should therefore treat most carbon footprint savings from recommended actions more as 'ballpark' figures than precise numbers, and even then some may be oversimplified or the benefits may not be clear-cut. For example, chickens reared indoors in cramped conditions are more efficient at converting their feed to meat than free-range birds. Intensively reared chicken therefore has a lower carbon footprint than free range, but at the cost of poorer animal welfare. For many people, eating less red meat (such as beef) may be more for health than environmental reasons. Another example is, while carbon savings from avoiding plastic carrier bags may be small, there is evidence that plastic waste is becoming a significant threat to sea birds and animals and hence it's a good reason for reducing the use of plastics for carrier bags and packaging. Such examples highlight that deciding between environmental actions may involve difficult trade-offs and just focusing on carbon footprints can leave out other environmental impacts.

Activity 3.6.   Light carbon living

Looking again at Tables 3.2 to 3.5 what would be most likely to substantially lighten your carbon footprint? And which seem to make only a small difference?

Discussion

The following actions listed in Tables 3.2 to 3.5 are more likely than others to significantly lighten your carbon footprint:

  reducing long car journeys (especially regular ones like commuting) or substituting them with bus or train travel

  improving home insulation (especially of older properties)

  avoiding air travel as much as possible

  keeping goods, rather than rapidly replacing them (except where a new product, e.g. a fridge or car, is significantly more energy efficient)

  reducing consumption of meat (especially beef) and dairy products

  replacing short car journeys with cycling (or walking) when possible.

The following actions are likely to have only a relatively minor effect on the carbon footprint, but can reduce other environmental impacts:

  recycling household waste

  avoiding use of plastic bags.

5.2 Lighter living costs and constraints

As well as Tables 3.2 – 3.5 there are resources available via the course website that provide more information on carbon emissions and savings of different actions. You can use this information to supplement the actions to lighten your carbon footprint indicated by a calculator.

But be careful not to double-count actions already covered by a calculator. For example, if you have already used a calculator that shows the approximate effect of generally improving home insulation, don't use the more detailed information in the tables or via the website to add the effect of, say, installing cavity or solid wall insulation. If possible, use the detailed information to estimate the effect of insulation improvements on the baseline (no improvements) figure from the calculator. See the *Guidance Notes* for more information.

The costs of 'light living' actions need, of course, also to be considered. Some actions involve no cost or save money, for example, less flying, shopping or meat eating, or can even make money, such as letting out a spare room to increase household occupancy. Others are low cost with a rapid *payback* time; for example, replacing an incandescent light bulb with a low-energy compact fluorescent lamp (CFL) should pay back the new lamp's cost in lower electricity bills in about 6 months. Other measures may involve extra cost, for example taking the train instead of driving, or considerable investment, such as installing a high-efficiency condensing boiler or solar water heating. Such big carbon-reduction benefits have to be weighed against affordability and costs (which may be changing quite rapidly).

Apart from cost, there are many other factors that may attract or deter you from some light living options. Travel behaviour is well known as one of the most difficult things to change. You may have little choice about using a car for commuting, shopping, or ferrying your children about. Looking forward to that foreign holiday may be the one thing that keeps you going.

As I noted in Section 2, your needs and wants and social values are important here. For example, some people feel that travelling by bicycle or bus is only for people who can't afford a car, and that flying to exotic destinations gives them social status. On the other hand, others find the idea of cutting their travel footprint in half, or making their home really 'green', exciting and challenging. As the final section shows, most people's lifestyles are only partly under their control: their freedom to change is constrained by their circumstances and the wider society. Even so, it's important not to fall into the trap that only making changes with relatively minor environmental benefits is enough: it's necessary to be willing to change more radically to tread lightly on the Earth.

5.3 Moving towards a sustainable carbon footprint

So far, you've been considering reductions in average individual or household carbon footprints by 20% to 30% or more.

But it is becoming increasingly clear that this will not be enough. As I mentioned in Section 4, developed countries, like Britain, Germany and America, will have to reduce their CO_2e emissions by 60% to 80% or more by 2050 to prevent climate change running out of control, while at the same time allowing the growing populations of Africa, India and China to reach reasonable standards of living.

A 60% reduction on an average 12.5 tonne UK footprint would be 5 tonnes CO_2e per person per year.* A 'Fair Share' carbon footprint of about 2.5 tonnes CO_2e per person per year (or less) has been suggested based on a contraction and convergence approach. This requires at least an 80% reduction on the average UK individual carbon footprint.**

Is it possible to achieve such large reductions without losing all the benefits of a developed country's consumer lifestyle? Some environmental pioneers have worked out how to do it and a few are already living lightly. Below are two case studies of households that are moving toward sustainability.

*12.5 tonnes $CO_2e \times (1.0 - 0.6) = 12.5 \times 0.4 = 5$ tonnes CO_2e

**$(12.5 - 2.5$ tonnes $CO_2e)/12.5$ tonnes $CO_2e \times 100 = 80\%$ (See Study note: *percentages* in Part 3)

Low carbon living

On the course DVD there are two case studies of UK households that are attempting to significantly lighten their carbon footprint, in the areas of energy, transport, food and goods consumption. The first shows the types of change that many people in a country like Britain could make, given sufficient funds. The second shows a more radical attempt at living lightly, which wouldn't suit everyone, but involves lower cost solutions.

View these case studies at a convenient time, preferably before moving to Part 4. Make notes on the behavioural and technical changes these households have made to lighten their carbon footprint and reduce other environmental impacts. (You could look again at Study note: *viewing for a purpose*, in Section 2.) Consider which (if any) of these changes you might consider yourself. After viewing, attempt the SAQs at the end of the section.

Low carbon living in an eco-renovated 1980s house

This video-based case study shows what a professional couple, Mark Luntley and Alice Brander, have done to eco-renovate their three-bedroom 1982 mid-terraced house in Oxford, as part of moving to a low carbon lifestyle. Below are some extracts based on their own account of what they did, plus some additional information I have added.

Read this background information before viewing the video, which lasts about 12 minutes.

(a)   (b)   (c)

(d)

Figure 3.14 (a) The front of the house; (b) the rear conservatory; (c) the boiler and solar heat store; (d) Toyota Prius hybrid petrol-electric car

Our philosophy

Our aim is to show how a modern family can make serious reductions in their environmental impact, whilst still having a standard of living most of us would recognise. Above everything our aim is to be practical, rather than offer solutions that few people are likely to adopt.

Energy

We started by commissioning an energy audit of our house. This showed our house was built to low, pre-1982 UK Building Regulations energy efficiency standards. Our plan of action included:

1 Replacing the ancient boiler with a modern condensing boiler and installing new heating controls and radiator valves.

2 Because of its cost, the case for installing solar water heating is usually marginal, but as we were having the central heating upgraded and the plumbers were in the loft we decided to go for it.

3 Insulation is key in any eco-renovation. We noticed the biggest change when we had the cavity walls filled with mineral fibre. We put sheep's wool insulation in the loft, 100 mm on top of the

70 mm of fibreglass, and insulated the walls and ceiling of the internal garage to stop heat leaking into the cold space.

4   Our house had single-glazed windows plus secondary glazing. We decided to install the best double-glazed windows we could, and then refit the existing secondary glazing – triple glazing for a fraction of the price.

5   Building a conservatory which helps to heat the house in spring and autumn and acts as a heat buffer in winter. The conservatory was the largest single investment we made, costing over £20 000. It's a great space for relaxing and growing plants, and it also improves the environmental performance of the house.

6   Building an insulated front porch to stop cold air entering the house in winter.

7   We cook, heat and provide hot water from gas. Our (2007) gas bills are around £7.50 per month. Electricity bills are about £32 per month, partly because Mark has been working from home recently and using his computer all day. Gas and electricity consumption is about 50% lower than when we first moved in.

One of the lessons Mark and Alice have learned is that planning eco-renovations is often easier than finding skilled contractors to do the work, although they eventually found some excellent tradespeople.

Water

We made an effort to save water. Lower hot water consumption also reduces energy use. Nationally, slightly more than a third of all domestic water is flushed down the toilet. A new UK toilet can use up to 9 litres a flush. We chose a Swedish design, which uses 2 and 4 litres a flush, but is indistinguishable from any other toilet.

Transport

We replaced our two cars with a Toyota Prius hybrid car. It cost little more than an average saloon, about £17 500 minus a £1000 government grant available at the time, yet uses less than half the fuel of the previous cars. It has two engines, one petrol, the other electric, whose battery is charged when the petrol engine is running and by recovering energy when going downhill or braking. We get around 55 to 63 miles per gallon (5 to 4.5 litres per 100 km) of petrol, and the (2008) car tax is £15 a year. Although the CO_2 emissions of the Prius are no lower than those of some super-mini diesel cars, it is a spacious family car, or as Mark says … 'it didn't mean driving a "noddy" car, or trading in comfort or safety'.

We've also got a couple of old bikes. These allow us to get around … without always jumping into the car.

We decided to live close to the city centre and to public transport. There's no point having a wonderful eco-house and having to travel long distances to and from work. Until recently … both of us could walk to work.

But now Alice works seven miles away in Abingdon and mainly commutes by bus, except when she needs the car to travel between two sites. Mark is changing jobs and may have to commute using their car, so Alice is exploring whether to get an electrically assisted bicycle for the days she needs personal transport.

Mark and Alice know that air travel is a very heavy polluter per passenger km. But Mark's brother lives in Canada, as do several of Alice's relatives, so they 'try to get over to that excellent country from time to time.' Mark acknowledges that their air travel to Canada about once every one to two years more than outweighs the CO_2 savings they've made from eco-renovating the house.

Food

Mark and Alice try to reduce their food impacts by various means. These include shopping in the local covered market for fresh, unpackaged food; using a box delivery service of locally grown vegetables; growing some fruit and vegetables on their allotment; buying local, ethically produced meat and eating it sparingly; and reducing their consumption of imported and out-of-season fruit and vegetables.

Goods and services

Living in a small house uses living space, and energy, efficiently. Mark and Alice like to keep the house uncluttered, which means not buying more goods than they really need or want and recycling unwanted items. As Mark says, 'reduce first, reuse second, and recycle third'.

Beyond the household

Mark and Alice try to reduce their carbon footprint as much as they can, but recognise that there are limits to what people can do individually. They therefore help others to follow their example by providing information, if asked by friends or colleagues, and by contributing to eco-renovation open days and websites.

At the community level, Mark is chair of the Westmill wind farm co-operative, which should generate more than enough electricity to supply the demand of all the co-op's 2500 members.

Mark and Alice also recognise that there are environmental issues that can only be tackled at government levels, such as local and regional planning and national energy, and transport policies. (These levels of individual, community and government responsibility are discussed further in Section 6 and in Part 4.)

(Mark Luntley and Alice Brander, personal communication and interviews March/April 2008)

The Yellow House

This multimedia-based case study shows what George Marshall, an environmental campaigner, has done to radically reduce his family's carbon footprint by eco-renovating a 1930s Oxford terraced house and living lightly. The Yellow House will give you an idea of the upper limit on energy saving that people living in most existing UK houses could make, using a combination of DIY and professional help, and without spending large amounts of money. (Note that homes built or substantially extended or renovated since 2006 are catching up with the energy performance standards of the Yellow House as a result of tighter UK building regulations and, as you'll learn in Part 4, are set to improve towards 'zero carbon' standards.)

(a)

(b)

(c)

Figure 3.15 (a) Front of the Yellow House, showing roof lights and solar panel; (b) dining room extension; (c) rear of the house showing sun porch

The case study also provides information on how to reduce environmental impacts in other areas, including: saving water; using recycled building materials and salvaged furniture; choosing household appliances, flooring and furnishing; reducing the impacts of food and cooking.

The Yellow House shows what can be done to eco-renovate a quite problematic UK property on a fairly limited budget.

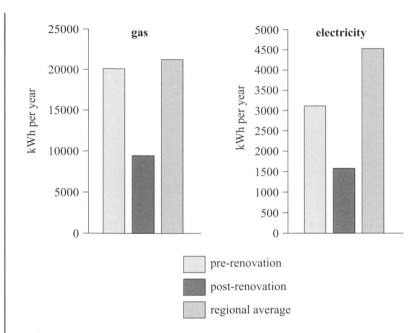

Figure 3.16 Annual gas and electricity use in the Yellow House have halved since eco-renovation. Electricity use is one-third of the regional average *(Source: Marshall, 2007b)*

George Marshall says little in this case study on transport, except 'we refuse to have a car and travel by bicycle and public transport … Managing without a car is a struggle in a world that assumes that all parents have cars.' However, since the birth of their second child, the Marshalls reluctantly bought a car, partly to be able to take their child, who suffers from asthma, to hospital at short notice.

The Yellow House case study is multimedia and includes four short videos, plus a lot of text and still pictures.

It contains far more material than you are required to study for this course.

Required viewing and reading

To view the required material:

1 Find the Yellow House material on the course DVD and view the four short sequences: 'Why we did it'; 'Kitchen and appliances'; etc., in total lasting about 10 minutes, in which George Marshall provides a good overview of the Yellow House project.

2 Access the Yellow House website content via the course website link. Then 'Tour the house'. I suggest that you tour in the following order: Downstairs – front of house; living room; kitchen; extension; utility room; back of house. Upstairs – bedroom; mezzanine; bathroom; office.

The tour is all text and pictures and should take no longer than 10 to 15 minutes.

During your tour, click on the hyperlinked sections containing additional detailed information only if you are interested. This material is optional, so don't spend your course study time accessing and reading it.

For more information see the Yellow House Guidance Notes.

Some cautionary notes on the Yellow House material

On the Yellow House videos George Marshall makes certain comments that raise some issues and controversies:

(1) Emissions from formaldehyde resin glues often employed for making chipboard, widely used for mass-produced kitchen cabinets, etc. can cause irritation to eyes, nose and throat. This is generally considered *not* to present a health hazard in the amounts present in chipboard. Chipboard also may be made from recycled timber and can last reasonably well. However, care should be taken when working with manufactured boards, especially medium density fibreboard (MDF), often used to make cabinet doors, which contains a higher proportion of formaldehyde resin.

(2) Putting extra insulation around fridges and freezers should only be done after fully checking whether the appliances are suitable and it is safe to do so; it is probably not worthwhile for recent, better insulated models. For example, only attempt to re-insulate appliances with *external* condenser coils and do not obstruct air flow over them. (There is more information in the optional reading – see below.)

(3) Recycling bath and shower water to flush toilets is possible, but should be done only after proper investigation and requires careful operation to avoid problems. (There is more information in the optional reading.)

(4) To prevent bacterial growth, it is recommended that hot water cylinder thermostats are set at 60 °C, rather than turned down to 50°C. Turning down the boiler thermostat to improve the efficiency of a *condensing* boiler could have the same effect (although the gains would have to be balanced against any increase in pump operation). However, problems in domestic systems from a lower hot water temperature are rare.

(5) External wall insulation should be specified by an architect or done by a qualified installer (or, as for the Yellow House, installed by a builder who knows the requirements of the job). Otherwise condensation or other problems could arise.

Optional reading

There are several sections of the Yellow House website containing optional, more detailed information as text and pictures (e.g. on Eco-principles; the Design Process, Insulation; Heating and Green Living).

The material in these sections is for those of you who are interested in exploring further the principles and practice of 'eco-conversion' of existing homes and may be planning to commission some energy efficiency or other improvements yourself. **However, the material is NOT intended as a do-it-yourself design or construction manual.** You should always seek professional help from a qualified architect and/or experienced builder and other qualified professionals (electricians, plumbers, etc.) when undertaking any practical work on your home, as well as obtaining planning permission and building regulations approval where required. The Building Control Department of your local council and the Energy Saving Trust can provide information.

See the Yellow House Guidance Notes for advice on accessing this optional content.

If you wish to consider eco-renovation (beyond the requirements of the course) there is additional material plus links to further sources of information on the course website.

SAQ 3.7

What transport dilemmas do Mark and Alice face in trying to live their low carbon lifestyle?

SAQ 3.8

(a) What approaches to saving direct energy for heating etc. have been adopted both by Mark and Alice in their house and by George in the Yellow House?

(b) What additional approaches to direct energy saving have been adopted in the Yellow House?

Activity 3.7   Moving towards sustainability (optional)

This is an optional Activity, if you have the time and interest, to explore, using the carbon calculator and/or the information in this section and the course website, how you might reduce your carbon footprint towards a sustainable or 'fair share' level.

The Activity involves investigating whether you can achieve a 60–80 percent, or more, reduction on an average individual carbon footprint (i.e. to at most 5 tonnes and preferably 2.5 tonnes or lower CO_2 equivalent per person if you live in the UK).

Summary of Section 5

Different 'light living' actions have very different effects on reducing individual or household carbon footprints. (For example, if you got carbon tokens for not using plastic carrier bags, you'd have to save over 300 000 bags to compensate for a return flight from Britain to Spain!)

A sustainable carbon footprint is likely to involve a reduction of 80%, or more, on the current average carbon footprint of the inhabitants of developed countries.

The most cost-effective light living actions include:

upgrading home insulation

reducing, or substituting, car and air travel

installing an efficient heating and hot water system

fully occupying homes (especially addressing the trend to one-person households)

reducing consumption of animal products and air-freighted fruits and vegetables

reducing purchases of high carbon goods and services (e.g. new vehicles, leisure activities involving high fossil fuel use and/or travel)

spending any spare income on low carbon goods and services (e.g. artworks or craft products, antiques or second-hand goods, services involving local labour, renewable energy technologies, carefully-chosen carbon offsets).

People's ability to make major light living changes is constrained by their circumstances, e.g. their jobs, family and willingness to change.

6 Who's responsible for lightening carbon footprints?

We must abandon the conceit that individual, isolated, private actions are the answer. They can and do help. But they will not take us far enough without collective action.

(Al Gore, 2007)

There are some things that we can do as individuals: making this an energy-efficient house and making smart transport choices. Then there are things that we can do in our community … I'm chair of a local community wind farm … and work with Low Carbon West Oxford, a group of local residents … And then there's a third strand where it's really much more to do with government.

(Mark Luntley, interview, April 2008)

6.1 'I', 'we' or 'they'?

In this part, you've seen that individuals and households directly or indirectly generate the demand for most of the goods and services produced and consumed in the economy.

Does this mean that individuals and households are responsible for reducing the CO_2 and other greenhouse gas emissions from all their *consumption*? Or are the businesses and industries that *produce* the goods and services mainly responsible? In this section we'll be considering who is responsible: 'I' (as an individual consumer or citizen), 'we' (my household, workgroup, community) or 'they' (the government, business, other countries, the European Union, and so on). In Part 4 you'll examine 'we' and 'they' more closely and be introduced to more formal terms for these categories (namely, 'civil society', 'market' and 'state').

6.2 The role of individuals and households

You've been considering how to reduce your own carbon footprint to help tackle the worst effects of climate and other environmental changes. To that extent, 'I' as an individual consumer has a role to play.

But unless you live alone, you share your household with other people, a group that could be called 'we'. Everyone in the household may have similar views on living lightly. But, even within a household, there may be different views and priorities about what, if anything, should be done about lightening carbon footprints. Saving energy and other resources can involve some inconvenience or loss of comfort and often involves advance planning or careful thought. It may involve spending money on carbon-saving products or cutting down on some pleasurable activities. There may be social or cultural issues, or deep-rooted beliefs and habits, which differ. Not everyone in the household may agree that the actions are necessary or desirable, or worth even minor inconveniences. Others may be driven by their environmental or other values to live as sustainably as possible.

Example: my household

Using a calculator to work out how to lighten my carbon footprint reminded me that some of these issues occur in my own household. For example, concerning energy use, my partner and her daughter like the house kept nice and warm in winter and often turn up the thermostat or thermostatic radiator valves.

On transport, while my partner and I run a small car, which we car-share to work and usually take a train or coach for longer journeys, my partner's daughter likes driving her own, fairly powerful, car and rarely uses public transport. And while my partner and I have avoided flying in the past year (having flown three times for leisure in the previous year), my partner's daughter has already enjoyed two holiday flights and is looking forward to a trip to Australia.

Concerning consumption, while I prefer buying a few long-lasting goods, my partner's daughter, and to some extent my partner too, like shopping for new things.

So while my own carbon footprint may be fairly light and could be lighter, the total household footprint is heavier than it could be. To lighten our footprint involves trade-offs and choices, and not getting into disagreements requires give and take among the household members.

You may be able to think of similar issues in your own household. Does this mean that each member of the household has to be responsible for their own carbon footprint? Or are there shared activities about which agreements and compromises have to be made in order to reduce the household's footprint?

Of course, you may not be just part of a shared household: you are also a member of society. Even if you agree within your household about what to do, many others in society are not concerned about reducing their carbon footprints. Is there any point in trying to reduce your footprint when others aren't interested or willing to change?

One view, argued by businessman and green politician Chris Goodall in *How to Live a Low-carbon Life* (2007), is that pioneering individuals have to take responsibility for significantly lightening their carbon footprints in an attempt to galvanise governments, businesses and other members of society into action. He admits that even a million individuals cannot tackle climate change alone, but since governments, businesses and others seem unwilling to make the necessary changes, they have to be persuaded by being shown successful examples of low-carbon living. His model is that of the abolition of slavery and votes for women, in which radical social and political change was brought about by the actions of small groups of highly committed people.

More positively, George Marshall, who eco-renovated the Yellow House, argues in his book *Carbon Detox* (Marshall, 2007a) that people who choose to live lightly are the smart pioneers of a new twenty-first century way of living that many people will want to copy in the future. It has been described as a process of 'viral social change'.

6.3 The role of active citizens and communities

Few people agree that individuals should take the main responsibility for tackling environmental issues. For example, in a 2007 poll of over 2000 UK citizens, 70% agreed that the government should take a lead in combating climate change, even if it means using the law to change people's behaviour. However, over 60% disagreed that there was nothing they could do to avert climate change and over half agreed that they would do more if others did more too, although 40% thought that recycling was the most effective action they could take (Downing and Ballantyne, 2007).

UK government policy is that individuals have an important role in reducing emissions. The individual and household role is mainly to help reduce direct carbon emissions, especially from home energy use and transport. The official 'Act On CO_2' carbon calculator thus focuses on these direct impacts, calculating the CO_2 emissions from heating and hot water, electronics and appliances, and car, motorcycle and air travel (DEFRA, 2008). However, the government's campaign Act On CO_2 also gives advice on other carbon-saving actions.

Part of the reason for these views and policies is that individual citizens don't control many of the decisions that affect their household's carbon footprint, especially decisions that affect indirect emissions, such as national energy and transport policies, town planning, food processing and retailing practices, overseas farming and manufacturing activities, and so on. In other words, while individuals and households are directly or indirectly responsible for most of the *consumption* of goods and services, they do not control their *production* and *distribution*.

It's usual therefore to allocate the duty for reducing environmental impacts to those parts of the national or global economy responsible for producing them, on the **polluter pays** principle. So, for example, an industry such as consumer electronics is normally considered to be responsible for reducing the emissions from its factories at home and abroad, within environmental regulations set by national governments and international organisations.

This is even though the industry is producing products such as TVs for final consumption by individuals and households, who make buying decisions (large or small screen, plasma or LCD technology, etc.) and thereby influence what is designed, made and sold.

Another reason why individuals argue that others are responsible for environmental problems is that people often feel powerless in the face of all the complex decisions and the big changes that seem necessary. However, even if they don't directly control many economic activities and policy decisions, in a democracy at least, individual citizens can influence some of them by voting in elections, involvement in pressure groups, charities, political parties, etc.

For example, an important factor that affects direct and indirect carbon footprints is the mix of sources used to supply energy – fossil fuels, nuclear power and renewable energy technologies such as wind turbines. Individuals can reduce their carbon footprint by generating some of their own renewable energy by installing *solar thermal* hot water panels or *solar photovoltaic* (PV) cells on the roof. More cheaply and simply, they can buy their electricity from a 'green' supplier that uses only renewable energy sources. But they can also have some influence on local or national energy planning, for instance through pressure groups campaigning for or against building large wind farms or nuclear power stations.

> If you want to find out more about renewable energy technologies see the course website.

Another way 'we' can lighten carbon footprints is by joining with others. For example, in the Oxford house case study in Section 5, I mentioned that Mark Luntley chairs a wind farm co-operative, owned by the members who invested in it. There are also a number of voluntary groups who get together to help each other reduce their individual and household impacts. Perhaps the longest established are the local environmental groups in the Netherlands, Germany and Britain set up through a charity called Global Action Plan (GAP), but new groups e.g. Transition Towns initiatives are emerging all the time, meeting both face to face and online. Government policy is to encourage such community environmental initiatives as being potentially as good, if not more effective, than individual action.

In the workplace, individual office workers can, of course, switch off lights and computers when not in use, recycle waste paper and so on. But surveys show that individuals are less likely to save energy at work than at home, as they don't have to pay the bills. However, by working with their colleagues, they can help each other to adopt green practices and also encourage their employer to adopt environmental policies, for example switching to a green electricity supplier, setting up recycling facilities, and establishing staff travel plans.

6.4 The role of governments and business

Despite all the possibilities for individual and group action to lighten carbon footprints, there will still be people, groups and organisations who will not be doing much. Many individuals limit themselves to 'every little bit helps', with relatively minor effects on their carbon footprint, like reusing plastic bags or recycling paper. This avoids having to consider more significant changes in car and air travel, home energy use, diet or shopping. Others will simply carry on producing and consuming to maximise their own personal or organisational benefit, even if they know this is to the detriment of everyone else and future generations.

*A term coined by an American ecologist Garrett Hardin in 1968

This behaviour is what has been called the *tragedy of the commons*.* The 'tragedy' is that for a long time each person, organisation or nation can gain an additional benefit by using or consuming a bit more of the commons (the Earth) until a resource is used up, or an irreversible environmental change has occurred. Then everyone suffers.

That's where government support and regulation, business initiatives and international agreements to tackle climate change and other environmental problems come in. It's what 'I' and 'we' can't achieve unaided and only 'they' have the power to do.

Such government, business and international actions include, in no particular order:

- international treaties on reducing greenhouse gas emissions
- national and international policies on increasing renewable energy supply
- EU regulations on energy labelling of refrigerators, washing machines, etc. and improving the energy performance of buildings
- EU agreements on improving vehicle fuel economy
- UK road taxation of cars depending on their CO_2 emissions
- UK building regulations on the energy performance of buildings, heating and lighting systems, and the UK's target of 'zero-carbon' new homes by 2016
- urban and regional planning polices to encourage people to use public transport
- local authority home insulation and heating improvement schemes
- company programmes to save energy, avoid waste and reduce car commuting
- environmental education and information programmes.

SAQ 3.9

(a) List five activities that 'I' could do effectively to reduce my own and others' carbon footprints. Include activities that I can do individually as a consumer or as an active citizen, and what 'we' could do as a household, workgroup or profession.

(b) Then list five activities that are beyond the control of individual consumers, citizens and social groups.

Summary of Section 6

There are limits to the ability of individuals and households to lighten carbon footprints, because individuals and households don't control decisions about the production and distribution of the goods and services they consume.

Even so, individuals can take many further actions as active citizens and/or members of a community organisation, a workgroup, profession, etc.

There are still many actions and activities concerning the environment beyond the control of individuals, households and communities. These require action by governments and business.

You'll be learning more about these 'civil society', 'state' and 'market' institutions in Part 4.

Summary of Part 3

This part of Block 1 has shown you that much of the carbon footprint of an economy is due to the direct and indirect use of energy and consumption of food, goods and services by individuals and households. Hence, what you can do as an individual consumer and/or household member to lighten your carbon footprint can be significant. But communities, business and governments also have a crucial role in tackling greenhouse gas emissions and climate change.

After completing Part 3 you should be able to:

- explain the nature and extent of the carbon footprint of individuals and households within the national and global economy
- assess your existing individual carbon footprint using a carbon calculator
- explore options for lightening your carbon footprint to given target levels using the calculator for computer modelling
- develop a short- and medium-term action plan for lightening your carbon footprint
- recognise the role of individuals and households in reducing national and global greenhouse gas emissions
- calculate percentages and means, round numbers appropriately and extract information from audio-visual materials.

Answers to SAQs

SAQ 3.1

(a) The carbon footprint is the total annual mass of 'carbon' emissions which result directly or indirectly from the activities of an individual or a group of people.

(b) 'Carbon' emissions can be measured as the annual mass in kilograms or tonnes of either: (i) carbon dioxide (CO_2) gas; or (ii) total greenhouse gases converted to carbon dioxide equivalents (CO_2e) in terms of their global warming potential; or (iii) the carbon (C) content of carbon dioxide gas.

SAQ 3.2

(a) Based on 2005 government information, the average UK individual's direct carbon footprint was $1.16 \times 44/12 = 4.25$ tonnes CO_2 per year.

(b) The two main components of the individual and household direct carbon footprint are CO_2 emissions from burning fossil fuels for (i) room and water heating and (ii) personal car travel.

(c) An example of the indirect carbon footprint of individuals and households you may have given is CO_2e emissions arising from the production and distribution of food, or the manufacture and supply of products such as cars and computers.

SAQ 3.3

The percentage reduction in the individual UK carbon footprint between 1990 and 2005 was $(13.4 - 12.3)/13.4 \times 100 = 1.1/13.4 \times 100 = 8.2\%$.

SAQ 3.4

(a) The programme says that the Carbons' household produces 45 tonnes of CO_2 a year.

(b) This works out at about 11 tonnes per person per year, for two adults and their two children. The average American's total carbon footprint is 20.4 tonnes CO_2 per person per year. As roughly half of the footprint is for home energy, transport and food, they could be living in the USA.

(c) The Carbons' footprint is nearly twice the UK carbon footprint of about 7 tonnes per person for home energy (3.1 tonnes), transport (2.8 tonnes) and food (1.1 tonnes) taken from Figure 3.5.

The video says that in China the Tans produce about one-seventh of the Carbons' emissions, or 1.6 tonnes per person per year direct emissions, but increasing as they move into their new energy-hungry apartment.

SAQ 3.5

(a) Actions suggested in The Carbons video to lighten, or at least to stabilise, the carbon footprint of households in developed countries include:

- buying more fuel-efficient cars
- halving personal car mileage and switching to public transport
- reducing room temperatures and wearing warmer clothes indoors
- switching to energy-saving light bulbs
- buying locally grown food
- composting food waste.

(b) The actions concerning car technology and use are likely to have a bigger effect than the suggested actions on energy and food. But, as is discussed in Sections 4 and 5, they are only a few of the many actions that individuals and households can take to lighten their carbon footprint.

(c) If every household (and office) made the most efficient energy and food choices over the next 50 years, that would cut one of Pacala's seven global warming slices or wedges. If personal car mileage were halved and the fuel economy of the world's cars was doubled, that could cut another two wedges over the same period.

SAQ 3.6

Here are some of the actions you may be able to model using a carbon calculator.

Technical – improving home insulation; using wood fuel for heating; buying, or changing to, a car with a smaller engine or using a different fuel.

Behavioural – lowering room temperatures; increasing the number of people occupying your household; changing to a 'green' electricity supplier; driving and flying less; using buses and trains, walking and cycling more; reducing consumption of meat and dairy products; recycling more; composting food waste.

SAQ 3.7

Mark and Alice's main transport dilemmas are:

- wishing to visit their relatives in Canada on average about once every one to two years, which involves flights that more than outweigh the carbon savings they've made from improving the energy performance of their house
- choosing low carbon transport for commuting, as the locations and requirements of their jobs change.

SAQ 3.8

The approaches to direct energy saving made by Mark Luntley and Alice Brander, and George Marshall include:

- insulation – as much as possible
- draughtproofing
- installing an efficient gas condensing boiler and controls
- building a solar conservatory and/or porch
- low energy lighting
- installing solar water heating
- efficient appliances and cooking with gas.

Additional approaches to direct energy saving in the Yellow House include:

- ventilation – careful control of air flows into warm and cool zones
- turning down thermostats and optimising boiler efficiency
- extra insulation around the freezer
- retaining waste warm water for toilet flushing.

SAQ 3.9

(a) You may have suggested some of the following:

What 'I' as an individual consumer and 'we' as a household could do to reduce our carbon footprints:

improve home insulation

install energy-saving lamps

change to a green electricity tariff

change to an energy-efficient condensing central heating boiler

drive and fly less often, or far

try to cycle, walk and use public transport more often

share car travel more often

change to a more fuel-efficient car

change diet to one with a lower environmental impact

spend less on high carbon goods and services.

What 'I' as an active citizen could do to reduce others' carbon footprints:

try to educate or persuade other household members, including children, to adopt more environmentally responsible behaviour

join an environmental support group (e.g. Global Action Plan) join an environmental pressure group

lobby local or national politicians on environmental issues

vote for a political party with the best environmental policies

try to save energy and resources at work

avoid unnecessary business travel, e.g. by telephone or computer conferencing.

What 'we' as a community, workgroup or profession could do to reduce our and others' carbon footprints:

work with local schools etc. to adopt environmental courses and policies

work with our employer to adopt environmental policies

act environmentally responsibly in our job.

(b) You may have suggested some of the following:

What 'they' as governments, etc. can do to reduce carbon footprints of the nation, region or world:

adopt policies to increase supplies of renewable sources of energy

develop and implement national, EU and international agreements and targets to reduce greenhouse gas emissions

develop and implement plans to reduce a business organisation's carbon footprint

adopt and implement regulations to improve the energy performance of buildings and the fuel economy of vehicles

introduce carbon taxes on businesses and industry

introduce a carbon-rationing scheme for individuals and households.

References

Baggott, S. L., Cardenas, L., Garnett, E., Jackson, J., Mobbs, D. C., Murrells, T., Passant, N., Thomson, A. and Watterson, J. D. (2007) *UK Greenhouse Gas Inventory, 1990 to 2005*, Harwell, Oxfordshire, AEA Technology.

Brower, M. and Leon, W. (1999) *The Consumer's Guide to Effective Environmental Choices*, New York, Three Rivers Press.

Cabinet Office (2007) *Policy Review: Energy and the Environment*, Prime Minister's Strategy Unit.

Carbon Trust (2006) *The Carbon Emissions Generated in All that We Consume*, London, The Carbon Trust.

Carbon Trust (2008) http://www.carbon-label.co.uk/product.html (Accessed October 2008).

CDIAC (2004) *Global, Regional, and National Fossil Fuel CO_2 Emissions*, US Department of Energy, Carbon Dioxide Analysis Centre, UN Statistics Division, Oak Ridge, TN, http://cdiac.ornl.gov/trends/emis/em_cont.htm (Accessed October 2007).

CEC (2008) *Proposal for a Decision of the European Parliament and of the Council on the Effort of Member States to Reduce their Greenhouse Gas Emission Reduction Commitments up to 2020*, Brussels, Commission for the European Communities, http://ec.europa.eu/environment/climat/pdf/draft_proposal_effort_sharing.pdf (Accessed March 2008).

Committee on Climate Change (2008) *Building a low-carbon economy – The UK's contribution to tackling climate change, First Report of the Committee on Climate Change*, London, The Stationery Office, December.

DEFRA (2006) *UK Climate Change Programme 2006*, London, Department for Environment, Food and Rural Affairs.

DEFRA (2007a) *UK Household and Population Figures 1970–2020*, Briefing Note BNXS25, Market Transformation Programme.

DEFRA (2007b) *Final Energy and Carbon Savings for the EEC 2008–11 Illustrative Mix*, London, Department for Environment, Food and Rural Affairs.

DEFRA (2007c) *Passenger Transport Emissions Factors. Methodology Paper*, London, Department for Environment, Food and Rural Affairs.

DEFRA (2008) *Act on CO_2 Calculator: Data, Methodology and Assumptions Paper*, version 2.1, London, Department for Environment, Food and Rural Affairs, http://www.defra.gov.uk/environment/climatechange/uk/individual/pdf/actonco2-calc-methodology.pdf (Accessed October 2008).

Downing, P. and Ballantyne, J. (2007) *Tipping Point or Turning Point?*, London, Ipsos MORI.

DTI (2007) *Meeting the Energy Challenge*, A White Paper on energy, London, The Stationery Office.

Dunster, B., Simmons, C. and Gilbert, B. (2008) *The ZEDbook: Solutions for a Shrinking World*, Abingdon, Taylor and Francis.

Ecobilan (2004) Report for Carrefour, Paris (in French), www.ademe.fr/htdocs/actualite/rapport_carrefour_post_revue_critique_v4.pdf (Accessed 22 September 2008).

EST (2008a) Energy Saving Trust, www.energysavingtrust.org.uk (Accessed May 2008).

EST (2008b) *Emission Impossible: a vision for a low carbon lifestyle by 2050*, Energy Saving Trust.

European Environment Agency (2005) *Household Consumption and the Environment*, EEA Report No 11/2005, Copenhagen.

Foster, C., Green, K., Bleda, M., Dewick, P., Evans, B., Flynn, A. and Mylan, J. (2006) *Environmental Impacts of Food Production and Consumption*. A report to the Department for Environment, Food and Rural Affairs by Manchester Business School, London, DEFRA.

Francis, P. (2004) *Impact of UK Households on the Environment through Direct and Indirect Generation of Greenhouse Gases*, London, Office for National Statistics, http://www.statistics.gov.uk/downloads/theme_environment/impact_of_households_final_report.pdf (Accessed May 2008).

Goodall, C. (2007) *How to Live a Low-carbon Life*, London, Earthscan.

Gore, A. (2007) *The Nobel Lecture given by The Nobel Peace Prize Laureate 2007*, 10 December 2007, Stockholm, The Nobel Foundation, http://nobelpeaceprize.org/eng_lect_2007c.html (Accessed 13 August 2008).

Haq, G., Minx, J., Whitelegg, J. and Owen, A. (2007) *Greening the Greys*, York, Stockholm Environment Institute, http://www.climatetalk.org.uk/downloads/ClimateChangeandOver50s.pdf (Accessed May 2008)

Hilty, L. M. and Ruddy, T. F. (2000) 'Towards a sustainable information society', *Informatik*, no. 4 (August), pp. 2–9.

HM Government (2007) *Building on Progress: Energy and Environment*, Policy Review, London, Prime Minister's Strategy Unit Cabinet Office.

HM Treasury (2006) Stern Review: *The Economics of Climate Change*, London, HM Treasury, http://www.hm-treasury.gov.uk/stern_review_climate_change.htm (Accessed 23 October 2008).

IPCC (2007) Summary for Policymakers. In *Climate Change 2007: Mitigation*. Contribution of Working Group III to the Fourth Assessment Report of the Intergovernmental Panel on Climate Change, Cambridge, Cambridge University Press.

MAFF (2000) *National Food Survey*, London, Ministry of Agriculture, Fisheries and Food.

Marshall, G. (2007a) *Carbon Detox. Your Step-by-Step Guide to Getting Real about Climate Change*, London, Gaia/Octopus Publishing.

Marshall, G. (2007b) The Yellow House: *Eco-renovation of a 1930s Terrace House, London,* presentation at Climate Change, Oxford, 5 June, Climate Outreach and Information Network, www.coinet.org.uk.

National Statistics (2007) *Environmental Accounts Autumn 2007*, Norwich, HMSO.

Open University (1983) T263 *Design: Processes and Products*, Block 2, 'Bicycles: Invention and Innovation', Milton Keynes, The Open University.

Tesco (2008) *How Can we Shrink our Carbon Footprint?*, www.tesco.com/greenerliving (Accessed May 2008).

Time for Change (n.d.) CO_2 *Emissions by Country*, http://www.timeforchange.org/co2-emissions-by-country (Accessed 7 August 2008).

Wallén, A., Brandt, N. and Wennersten, R. (2004) 'Does the Swedish consumer's choice of food influence greenhouse gas emissions?' *Environmental Science and Policy*, vol. 7, pp. 524–35.

Worldmapper (2008a) 'Greenhouse Gases', Map No. 299, http://www.worldmapper.org/display.php?selected=299 (Accessed 16 December 2008).

Worldmapper (2008b) 'Land Area', Map No. 1, http://www.worldmapper.org/display.php?selected=1 (Accessed 16 December 2008).

WRAP (2006) *Environmental Benefits of Recycling: an international review of life cycle comparisons for key materials in the UK recycling sector*, Waste & Resources Action Programme, http://www.wrap.org.uk (Accessed November 2008)

WRAP (2008) *The food we waste*, Waste & Resources Action Programme, http://www.wrap.org.uk (Accessed November 2008).

WWF (2006) *Ecological Budget UK: Counting Consumption*, Goldalming, Surrey, World Wide Fund for Nature-UK, p. 9.

Part 4
Building towards sustainability

Joe Smith

Introduction

1

Can individual actions 'save the world'? While the kinds of actions laid out in Part 3 can make an important contribution, they will not in themselves be sufficient to address global environmental problems. In this part you will take a closer look at the ideas and work of some of the people and institutions that have the power to move not just one household, but whole societies towards a more sustainable state. This part concentrates on the built environment: towns, cities and individual buildings. Buildings and settlements protect us from 'the elements'. They have served as a kind of second skin, and provided the *oikos*, or household (recall the discussion of this Greek word at the beginning of Part 2), within which human culture has flourished. Global warming and other environmental changes mean that over the next few decades all buildings and settlements are going to have to change. They will have to be adapted to cope with a changing climate, but the construction industries and professions will also have to greatly reduce polluting and wasteful practices. Cities, towns and buildings will all have to become more sustainable. As the image of Los Angeles from the air at night (Figure 4.1) suggests, the challenge of achieving a more sustainable built environment is enormous.

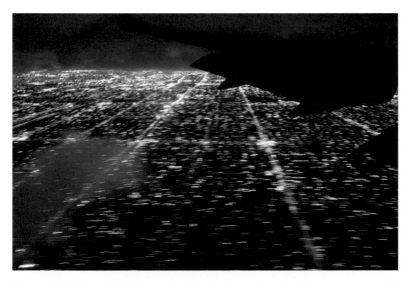

Figure 4.1 The night view of any city from the air gives a sense of the scale of the challenge of making settlements more sustainable. Los Angeles, a city designed for the car, is a particularly demanding example

Since the late 1980s the issue of climate change has made the search for more sustainable ways of doing things more urgent. However, climate change and sustainable development are very big concepts. The following sections focus on particular communications or decision-making tools. They also provide case studies of specific building projects and construction-related policies to see how practical progress on these challenges can be made at a level above

171

the individual household. Although I don't always use the phrase 'sustainable development', all of the ideas and case studies can be understood as attempts to simultaneously recognise social, environmental and economic interests. In other words, they are all attempts at achieving 'win–win–win' outcomes, and making progress towards sustainable development.

Although this part of Block 1 moves away from the household focus of Part 3, it does not signal a 'handing over' of the challenge of sustainability to business or government. One of the difficult – but fascinating – things about action on environmental change is the fact that both the generation of problems, and the responsibility to respond, are widely shared. Sometimes in environmental debates it is possible to hear engineers insist on technical solutions, marketing 'gurus' stressing behavioural changes, or economists claiming that the solution lies in 'getting the price right' in relation to pollution or resources. Some argue that solutions are rooted in millions of individual decisions to alter lifestyle; others believe that only strong political leadership can deliver. It is worth pausing to reflect on the distinction between 'I', 'we' and 'they' used in Part 3 and try to find more precise terms. One approach is to think in terms of three interlocking spheres: the *state*, the *market* and *civil society*. These are discussed in Box 4.1.

Box 4.1   The state, the market and civil society

Sociologists, political scientists and others have looked for ways of distinguishing the range of institutions that influence daily life with more precise categories. One simple set of distinctions is between 'state', 'market' and 'civil society'. This three-way division has stood the test of time: it was first sketched out in the late eighteenth century. The state points to those institutions that enjoy the power to make and maintain laws (parliaments, law courts), that have a monopoly on the use of force within a country (police, army) and the power to set and raise taxes.

The market sphere is that of private capital, above all companies. The civil society sphere contains voluntarily joined institutions that bring together citizens independently of the state and market spheres (e.g. most environmental *non-governmental organisations* (hereafter shortened to NGO) and community or religious groups). The private sphere of the family is notionally separate from these other larger institutions, although there can be considerable overlap. Figure 4.2 shows one way of representing the three spheres of state, market and civil society. The intersections between the three reflect the fact that there are some 'grey areas' where an institution or activity doesn't easily fall wholly in one sphere.

The ways 'they' was categorised in Part 3 generally means state or market. The category 'we' often indicates civil society institutions (though not always). 'I' is interesting: a public-sector worker may feel part of the state in their day job, but belong to a church group or NGO; they might also earn some money from trading on the internet (e.g. eBay or share trading) in their spare time and hence identify themselves as also being part of the institutions in the market sphere. Movement towards a more sustainable society will not be achieved unless all of these spheres are very actively engaged.

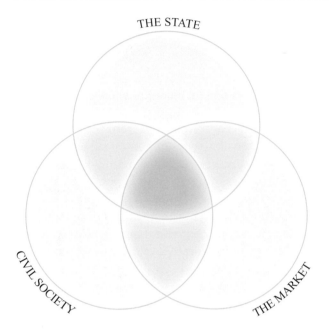

THE STATE

CIVIL SOCIETY

THE MARKET

Figure 4.2 Who has responsibility for action on sustainability: The State, The Market or Civil Society? This Venn diagram is one way of demonstrating the different institutions that can play a role in enabling or inhibiting action; it shows how they overlap

Study note: introducing Venn diagrams

Figures 4.2 and 4.3, with their three interlocking circles, are known as a Venn diagram. Such diagrams were invented in 1880 by the English mathematician and philosopher, John Venn. They offer a straightforward way of showing the logical relationships between families of things, or sets. These diagrams almost always show overlapping circles, and are often used to prove simple logical arguments. You may have seen something like the three-set diagram in Figure 4.3(b) before.

Any items under consideration that fit exclusively in one family or set are placed in the yellow area in this particular Venn diagram ('1 set'); any that meet the criteria of fitting in two families or sets are coloured red ('2-sets') and those that are considered members of all three families or sets are placed in the blue area ('3-sets'). Note that the colours are arbitrary. In other Venn diagrams there may be no colouring or shading.

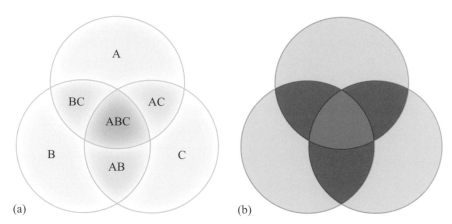

Figure 4.3 Venn diagram using (a) labels and (b) colour to show sets

The Venn diagram in Figure 4.2 has been used to represent the range of people and institutions with responsibility for action on sustainable development. It allows you to get a quick sense of the main boundaries between three distinctly different kinds of institution. This graphical technique allows you to see very quickly that states, markets and civil societies are distinct but overlapping clusters of institutions of contemporary societies. It is worth noting, however, that social and political phenomena are impossible to fully capture in graphical form or mathematical formulae. Social scientists and political theorists tend to be much more comfortable with written arguments that allow for more complexity and uncertainty in drawing boundaries and describing change. Nevertheless it remains a useful way of sketching out some key distinctions and relationships between categories.

This part, and the course as a whole, won't refer very frequently to the terms state, market and civil society, but you may find it helpful to keep these distinctions in mind as you consider the divisions of responsibility for action on environmental change. The Venn diagram makes a useful stepping-off point into a part of the course that looks at strategies for approaching system-wide change. You will return to use the technique at the end of this part, within an SAQ that is about who is responsible for leadership on sustainable construction.

The part first looks specifically at carbon emissions, in this case in terms of 'wedges' of emissions reductions. Note that the supporting video *The Carbons and Pacala's wedges* (which you should already have viewed in Part 3) used the term 'slices' to express the same idea. It then focuses more closely on an example of a decision tool intended to make the construction of buildings more sustainable, namely the 'One Planet Living' concept. Next it looks at examples of building projects that lay claim to being more sustainable, and the final, shorter, section considers the UK government's ambitious policies for 'zero carbon homes'. The story this part tells focuses on debates, experiments and cases in the UK, but the principles are globally relevant.

Coping with climate change – one wedge at a time

2

2.1 Pacala and Socolow's wedges

One of the central problems for both policymakers and the publics they have to answer to in approaching climate change is the sheer scale and pervasiveness of the issue. The causes and consequences of climate change reach into every aspect of life. It feels like an insurmountable challenge. Cutting carbon dioxide and other greenhouse gas emissions has been recognised by almost all senior political figures internationally as an important policy goal, but progress has been slow.

(a)   (b)

Figure 4.4 Physicist Robert Socolow (a) and ecologist Stephen Pacala (b) created the carbon wedges approach to help break the challenge of carbon emissions reductions into manageable wedges.

To help both policymakers and publics feel that 'this is a problem we can fix', a pair of American academics, Steve Pacala and Robert Socolow (pictured in Figure 4.4; you have also come across Pacala in the video *The Carbons and Pacala's wedges*) worked out a new way of presenting the options facing society. Their wedges approach, shown in Figure 4.5, is designed to:

- make progress on cutting carbon dioxide emissions seem practical and achievable

- show that significant emissions reductions can be achieved using technology that is already in existence.

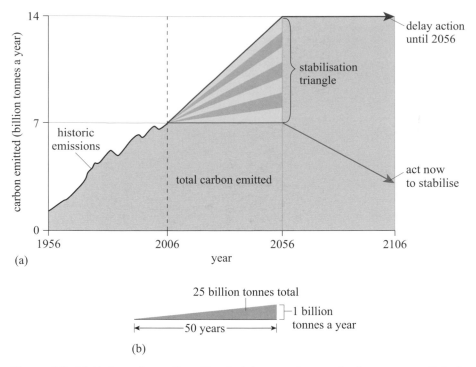

(a)

(b)

Figure 4.5 (a) Unless dramatic action is taken, carbon emissions are predicted to grow rapidly in the next fifty years. But the wedges model shows how the task of emissions reduction can be broken down into a series of wedges. Decisions on how many 'wedges' will be needed, and which they will be, must combine science and politics; **(b) One wedge equals one billion tonnes carbon emissions reductions per year (or 3.7 billion tonnes CO$_2$ per year)** *(Source: adapted from Socolow and Pacala, 2006)*

Figure 4.5(a) compares two possible global 'carbon' futures. The first, shown by the upper ('delay action until 2056') path, assumes that anthropogenic carbon dioxide emissions grow at the pace of recent years for the next 50 years and are then held steady. The lower ('act now to stabilise') path, shows emissions frozen at recent levels for 50 years and then reducing over time. The total amount of carbon released into the atmosphere by human activity is represented by the shaded area and is a rough guide to the total carbon dioxide concentrations eventually found in the atmosphere. The upper path, which represents a 'let's carry on as before until 2056' approach, would eventually set in train the more alarming consequences described at the end of Part 2. The lower path, which requires action now, would allow carbon dioxide concentrations in the atmosphere to stabilise, though at a much higher level than today (Figure 4.6).

In Figure 4.5(a) the difference between the two paths, the stabilisation triangle, represents the additional carbon emissions predicted for the next fifty years unless habits, policies and technologies change. As time goes by the 'carbon' gap between these two paths increases and the challenge of reducing carbon emissions grows greater. To make the task of bridging this gap appear achievable, Socolow and Pacala suggest splitting the

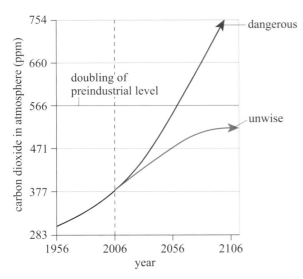

Figure 4.6 Action now would allow carbon dioxide concentrations in the atmosphere to stabilise (*Source: adapted from Socolow and Pacala, 2006*)

stabilisation triangle into manageable portions or wedges, where each wedge represents the reduction of carbon emissions from a specific technical or policy initiative. In the figure it is divided into seven wedges represented by the thinner triangles. The time frame and size of the wedges match what could be achieved in practice by a major technical or policy proposal. As Figure 4.5(b) shows, each wedge represents a reduction in emissions of 25 billion tonnes of carbon over fifty years at a rate of removal that reaches one billion tonnes per year by the end of the period.

Figure 4.6 shows the two paths from Figure 4.5(a) translated into forecasts for concentrations of carbon dioxide in the atmosphere over the next hundred years. The upper path leads to levels that many describe as dangerous. The lower path leads to doubling of the levels found before industrialisation, described as 'merely unwise' by Socolow and Pacala (Socolow and Pacala, 2006).

The numbers used in the original proposal have been overtaken by events and advances in modelling, but its purpose – to show *how* to achieve reductions – has not. Today, instead of holding global emissions constant until the 2050s, NGOs and governments are discussing how to reduce them by between 60 and 90 per cent to avoid the more dangerous impacts from climate change. The wedge approach can still be used to explore how to reach these new targets, but clearly many more wedges will need to be found.

The precise relationship between carbon emissions and concentrations of carbon dioxide in the atmosphere, shown in Figures 4.5(a) and 4.6, is not easy to visualise, but can be modelled.

> The next time you go to your computer you may wish to explore the wedges concept further by spending half an hour experimenting with the interactive charts on the course DVD.

Based on the wedge approach, you can examine the effects of taking action sooner or later, and of different sizes of carbon cuts.

You can change the values in terms of both the number of wedges and the year in which additional wedges are added. By looking at one chart you can see the effects of different numbers of wedges and 'start dates' of carbon emissions decline. In the other you can see the effects of the wedges on carbon dioxide concentrations in parts per million in the atmosphere, indicating temperature. As you learned in Part 2, it is the increasing carbon dioxide concentrations in the atmosphere, expressed as parts per million, that are ultimately making the biggest contribution to changing the climate.

I also recommend that you view The Carbons and Pacala's wedges video again.

Box 4.2	What is 'dangerous' climate change?

Now and again in this course and the media you will come across the phrase 'dangerous climate change'. Indeed, one of the key aims of the **United Nations Framework Convention on Climate Change** (hereafter UN FCCC) is 'to achieve … stabilization of greenhouse gas concentrations in the atmosphere at a level that would prevent dangerous anthropogenic interference with the climate system' (United Nations (1992) Article 2). Many propose that limiting climate change to 2 °C of warming above pre-industrial levels will avoid the most severe consequences of climate change. Others suggest 3 °C might be manageable.

Some of the terms you come across in the course are used to indicate well-researched scientific fact. Scientific and technical terms, whether on the global level such as 'parts per million carbon dioxide' or global mean surface temperature, or the very local physics of home insulation you met in Parts 2 and 3, are clearly defined and measurable. However, the definition of 'dangerous' in this case is very different. Scholars and students need to apply a different set of skills when they interpret what lies behind the term.

It is important to recognise that danger is a culturally and politically determined concept. It is not a static or universal definition. Furthermore, there are different categories of danger arising from climate change. The threat of abrupt changes in the climate system (sometimes called tipping points) presents one kind of danger. However, relatively gradual changes in climate in some agricultural areas could seriously affect food security. Figure 2.16, adapted from the Stern Review, in Part 2 indicates the range of dangers. It also usefully shows how the dangers change in character and intensity over time.

The hazards of climate change present very different dangers to wealthy and poor countries. That fact is rooted in the capacity to adapt. The wealthy may more easily afford adaptation measures (although some have pointed out that the poor are already better at adapting to environmental change). In other words, the danger to Bangladeshis living in the Ganges delta is different from the danger to East Anglian farmers with land on the coast. Although an English farmer may have less experience of having to adapt to environmental changes, they have many more financial and other resources with which to cope. For the Bangladeshi, storms and sea-level rise may combine to mean a matter of life and death. Similarly, the hazards facing those that live in hotter climates are far greater than those living in temperate climates such as northern Europe.

One of the challenges for climate change policymaking and communications is that the dangers might be decades in the future. However, elections might be months away and the danger of losing an election through, for example, raising carbon taxes, more pressing. Climate change campaigners work to bring these future dangers into the present, and to bring some urgency into political debates (see Figure 4.7). On the other hand, some commentators argue that the dangers are exaggerated and radical actions are not justified.

Figure 4.7 Defining dangerous climate change is an inherently political task. These campaigners make claim to the scientific roots of their cause, but also make an emotional appeal with their photographs of notional future victims of climate impacts

One of the things that Pacala and Socolow wanted their 'wedges' idea to achieve was to give a sense to United States politicians, policy experts and the public that addressing climate change was a manageable challenge, and one that involved choices. Hence they did not promote particular actions in their paper, but instead suggested that the wedges could be selected from a menu of options.

In their original 2004 paper in the internationally respected academic journal *Science* they put forward fifteen specific wedge strategies for cutting carbon emissions (Pacala and Socolow, 2004), for example using best efficiency practices in all residential and commercial buildings (Figure 4.8). However, there is nothing magic about the number fifteen; indeed in their schools and public education materials, and online, they encourage people to propose alternatives. Their fifteen wedge strategies are grouped under eight broader categories or headings, for example improving energy efficiency, using wind energy or solar energy, as in Figure 4.8. This figure has been reproduced from their materials. Note that it does not matter that you may not have come across all of the terms that appear in that figure. It is not important that you are familiar with all the concepts or technologies, although some, such as **carbon capture and storage**, are shown briefly in *The Carbons and Pacala's wedges* video. The key thing at this point is to follow the argument that action on climate change is about making choices. It is about balancing the costs and benefits of different options.

Note that some of the eight categories include plenty of different ways to reduce emissions reductions. For example, most of the ideas contained in Part 3 on reducing a household's carbon footprint would be found in the 'efficiency' category. Many of the actions you studied in Part 3 and in your work on the carbon calculator would fall into that bracket.

The authors argue that all of their 15 'wedge' options are practical, even if some have not yet been demonstrated on a large or economic scale, including for example carbon capture and storage. In some cases this means that the technology has been tested in the marketplace and, in the context of fossil fuels becoming more expensive, has been found to be increasingly economic (e.g. fuel switching, renewable sources of energy ('**renewables**'), nuclear power; for more information on the pros and cons of these options see the course website). Others have been shown through research to be plausible with further research and commercial development. Some wedges have been shown to work as good business practice or housekeeping, especially in the context of government support (energy efficiency and conservation). Each wedge throws up its own challenges – some political, some technical, some social. Many of them require that controversial decisions are made in advance of their introduction.

Efficiency

1. Double fuel efficiency of 2 billion cars from 30 to 60 mpg
2. Decrease the number of car miles travelled by half
3. Use best efficiency practices in all residential and commercial buildings
4. Produce current coal-based electricity with twice today's efficiency

Fuel Switching

5. Replace 1400 coal electric plants with natural gas-powered facilities

Carbon Capture and Storage

6. Capture AND store emissions from 800 coal electric plants
7. Produce hydrogen from coal at six times today's rate AND store the captured CO_2
8. Capture carbon from 180 coal-to-synfuels plants AND store the CO_2

Nuclear

9. Add double the current global nuclear capacity to replace coal-based electricity

Wind

10. Increase wind electricity capacity by 30 times relative to today, for a total of 2 million large wind turbines

Solar

11. Install 700 times the current capacity of solar electricity
12. Use 40 000 square kilometres of solar panels (or 4 million wind turbines) to produce hydrogen for fuel cell cars

Biomass Fuels

13. Increase ethanol production 30 times by creating biomass plantations with area equal to one-sixth of world cropland

Natural Sinks

14. Eliminate tropical deforestation AND
15. Adopt conservation tillage in all agricultural soils worldwide

Figure 4.8 The wedges approach presents choices, with different costs and benefits. The figure shows 15 wedges, listed under eight different categories.

Activity 4.1   Pick three wedges: are they state, market or civil society led?

Using the blank table below, pick three wedges from Figure 4.8 or include others (perhaps derived from actions to lighten your carbon footprint in Part 3) to fill the left-hand column. In the right-hand column, state whether they are challenges that primarily require action by civil society (e.g. community, NGO, union or school), the market (business) or the state (local or national government, international organisation). Don't be afraid of being simplistic or 'broad brush'. The intention here is to get a quick sense of where responsibility lies for action on the different wedges. You might want to flesh out your right-hand column with a sentence or two that explains what the nature of the actions (projects, programmes or policies) that deliver the wedge might be. You may want to look back at Box 4.1, where the terms state, market and civil society are explained, and Figure 4.2, where their roles and interactions relating to sustainability are represented using a Venn diagram.

Wedges	State; market; civil society?

Discussion

Here is my effort. I found myself mixing market, state and civil society actions. In contrast with the measures discussed in Part 3, most of these wedges tend to be actions that government or industry must lead on.

Wedges	State; market; civil society?
Double fuel efficiency of 2 billion cars from 30 to 60 mpg	In terms of state–market mix this is likely to involve the state influencing market conditions through policy, but the market doing most of the work in communicating these signals. Most efficiency gains have to be delivered via technology developed by the car industry, probably catalysed by government regulations (e.g. US or EU) and helped by government investments in applied research. Individual ('I') actions count too, ranging from driving style to regularity of servicing and choice of vehicle. In fact this wedge illustrates how individual, civil society, state and market often interact; vehicle licensing and taxation legislation is shown to boost the market for efficient vehicles. Pressure from civil society institutions such as NGOs and community groups can help to create a political climate for change.
Use best efficiency practices in all residential and commercial buildings	State leadership through national and EU regulation is likely to do most of the 'heavy lifting' here in raising building standards and the performance of the construction industries. Although individual choices make a difference for a small percentage of individual 'pioneer' households and communities, most efficiency gains in this sector will be delivered by state and market measures. These might include e.g. government regulation setting ever-higher standards for built-environment professionals and the construction industry in the production of new buildings. Increasing efficiency of existing buildings can be encouraged through increasing the cost of fossil fuel and regulating energy suppliers to promote efficiency measures in homes. Business is a key partner in delivering these policies.
Install 700 times the current capacity of solar electricity	Again a state–market mix, with governments setting the conditions and business finding efficient (profitable) ways of achieving change. Pioneering individual householders and businesses have helped to demonstrate the potential of installing solar PV roofs. Major expansion of solar capacity relies on a partnership. Governments can send clear signals about fossil fuel prices going up and perhaps incentives for installing renewables, and business and the research community can respond with new technologies, applications and financing. One can happen without the other, but everything will move faster if there is an integrated mix of state and market action.

There are plenty of attractive things about the wedges approach. It shows that stabilising and then reducing carbon emissions is a problem that can be addressed: the authors based the wedges on using or scaling up existing technologies. It breaks carbon emissions reductions into manageable chunks, and allows each of them to be considered in terms of cost, pace of introduction and risk. The wedges approach doesn't favour just one from the list of government intervention, technology fixes, social change or market measures as 'the' answer. Rather it outlines a mix of paths where these often combine. They offer a menu of options that can be sorted according to different criteria – be it cost, political acceptability or speed of implementation. The authors argue that this approach helps to build consensus for action.

Although challenging in some ways, the wedges approach also delivers some good news to the developing world. These countries could *leapfrog* the dirty industrial development of the developed countries by introducing advanced technologies first. Taking this line, the developing world could be the origin of technologies that could favour low or zero carbon development everywhere. However, to do so would require compensation or investment for the 'first movers' – those taking the first risks. Pacala and Socolow see this kind of leapfrogging as a path to 'globally coordinated mitigation'. However, there are pitfalls too, many of which the authors anticipate. Here are just some of the challenges associated with some of the specific wedge proposals:

- The world will need institutions that set and communicate a reliable (increasing) global price for carbon or *carbon pricing* (through measures such as carbon trading or taxing or regulation).

- If the nuclear power wedge is chosen, strong international enforcement will be needed to control the further spread of nuclear weapons.

- If carbon capture and storage wedges are pursued, there will need to be widespread permission for geological storage of the captured carbon (e.g. as a liquefied gas).

- Renewable energy and carbon sink management (meaning, for example, the protection and extension of carbon sinks such as tropical forests) will need extensive land reclamation or reassignment.

- Pursuit of *biofuels* made from agricultural crops will raise food prices and affect availability and/or accelerate biodiversity loss, for example as forests are turned over to biofuels plantations.

- If hydrogen is to be widely used, e.g. as a vehicle fuel, the safety issues will need to be addressed.

- If alternative fuel vehicles are widely adopted (e.g. by renewable electricity-powered battery technologies, hydrogen or biofuels) then congestion and other downsides of private transport will still need to be addressed.

SAQ 4.1 What are wedges of CO_2 emissions reductions?

Check your understanding of the 'wedges' approach to CO_2 emissions reductions with answers to the following questions:

How much carbon emissions reduction does each wedge represent?

How many billion tonnes of carbon will be emitted per year in 2056 if no action to reduce carbon emissions is taken (in other words, where will a 'business as usual' scenario leave the level of emissions)?

2.2 Critiques of the wedges approach: climate change = politics

There are criticisms to be made not just of the individual proposals, but of the whole wedges approach. The model was developed by American academics, and was almost certainly targeted at that country's political and policy communities at a time when the US was seen as lagging in its commitment to action on climate change. It was intended to move the debate on by demonstrating that action on addressing climate change is both possible and practical using existing technologies. However, there is a danger that people might be led into underestimating the size of the political task in pursuing significant emissions reductions. The cool, rational wedges approach might disguise the intensity of future conflicts concerning different routes to emissions reductions.

The wedges approach is attractive as a communications tool, and it helps make space for a debate, but some American politicians and commentators have dismissed the wedges approach as being far too rough and ready to inform such a dramatic change in energy, climate and economic policy. They charge the authors with taking a very broad brush to their canvas in ways that suit the academic seminar room, but are of little value when it comes to running one of the world's great economies. There is a feeling that the economic and social costs to the United States of taking action on most of these wedges cannot be borne in the near term, either by the economy or by the American electorate. George Bush Sr made this point very bluntly as US President at the 1992 Earth Summit, where he was reported as saying that 'the American way of life is not up for negotiation' (McKibben, 2002). Some leading politicians still hold to a similar line.

A more subtle point has been made by some economists and other commentators who argue against interventions in the economy. They feel that governments shouldn't limit any form of wealth creation in the present. They suggest that, on the basis of past experience, rapid economic growth delivers the speediest route to technology improvements. They suggest that free markets will deliver much faster emissions reductions with no economic cost, and that political focus on climate change is a distraction from other problems that need international attention, such as clean water supplies or health provision. Their argument on technology is that in a fiercely competitive global marketplace firms will work hard to innovate. This is because new products and services reach new markets, but can also serve to bring costs down. The free-market optimists insist that these virtues of unfettered capitalism will inevitably lead to the most efficient emissions reductions. Put another way, they fill the triangle of emissions reductions between 2006 and 2056 with one great big wedge: economic growth.

A similar argument is put by 'technological optimists'. It has been pointed out that the wedges approach focuses on existing technologies, but one can look at the last fifty years of startling technological development and suggest that there will be some very positive surprises in store if there is investment in new technologies. In the context of political agreements it is easy to imagine researchers, entrepreneurs and politicians creating the conditions for previously unimagined means of driving down emissions.

A separate critique is that the rosy hopefulness of the wedges approach denies both the urgency of the issues and the extent of political conflict ahead. Radical environmentalists argue that humanity must ready itself for much more dramatic change in developed world economies and lifestyles. Some argue the need to factor in hazardous physical changes that will come with climate change that will impact upon some of the wedges. They ask questions such as: 'Is it wise to place new nuclear power stations in coastal areas, given the increased likelihood of flooding and sea-level rise?'

Much of the rhetoric of sustainable development seems to imply that there is an easy consensus on the need for action, and agreement on the partnerships that will be needed. However, this denies the very real conflicts and debates that environmental issues generate. It is not enough to simply recognise that states, markets and civil society all hold responsibilities for action. With responsibility widely distributed, how will progress be made, and who is going to hold people to account? The Wal-Mart executives who invested in the solar roof in Figure 4.9 and the activists organising climate camps, such as the one advertised in Figure 4.10, have very different answers to those questions.

Figure 4.9 Large companies like Wal-Mart are being driven by both customers and fuel prices to invest in low-carbon developments. The solar roof on this Palm Desert store will supply up to 30% of the building's energy needs. Some argue that unregulated markets are the fastest, most cost-effective route to CO_2 emissions reductions.

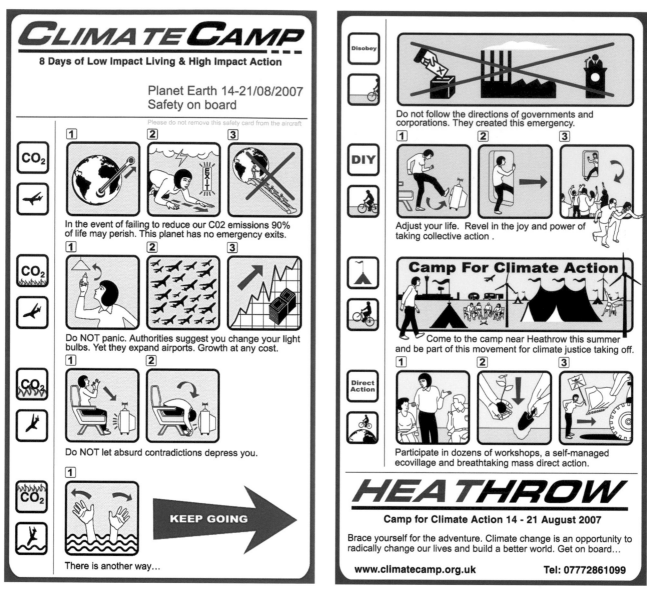

Figure 4.10 Environmental issues have always introduced new ways of doing politics. The UK's climate camps have brought together a loose network of mostly young people for non-violent direct action and often-witty critiques of current policy. This mock airline safety leaflet was part of the publicity for a camp at Heathrow Airport in 2007.

Activity 4.2   How do you think about the future?

Take a look at this range of statements and see if you can place yourself within one or more of these camps of opinion. You may want to get friends or family to place themselves in relation to these statements too. There is likely to be quite a wide spread of opinion.

- Economic optimist: we don't need to act on climate change – the run of the free market is already the most efficient method of driving down emissions.

- Technological optimist: all we need to do is encourage new technology research, development and investment, or put a price on carbon to see new sustainability-inspired industries grow like weeds.

- Clever state–market mix: with a judicious blend of market signals (e.g. increased fossil fuel prices) and regulations (e.g. efficiency standards) we'll arrive at politically acceptable and economically viable responses to climate change.

- Government intervention: everyone from business to householders are crying out for political leadership that will create a fair situation that strongly favours low- and zero-carbon options in e.g. transport, and household and business energy use.

- Social/ecological pessimist: human societies are not capable of acting to avoid dangerous climate change and the environmental processes underlying climate change may have gone so far already that nothing humans do can make a difference. The best we can do is to prepare to adapt.

- Climate change sceptic: swimming against the current of 'mainstream' scientific and political opinion, the sceptic is convinced that climate change is at best over-hyped and possibly an invention of self-interested science and policy experts.

Discussion

It may be difficult to place yourself exclusively in one or another camp, but laying out these different positions does help to explain some of the conflicts of interest and diverse perspectives that underlie many environmental issues. On one day the news of an exciting development in hydrogen fuel cell technology might seem to suggest the technological optimist has all the answers. On another you might look out on a long queue of traffic or see the refuse truck go by fully loaded and argue that dramatic change in policy is the only way to change wasteful developed world lifestyles. Most EU governments are hoping that they can walk the tightrope with a 'clever market–policy mix' route. It leaves the status quo mostly intact in terms of government and business, but they hope it will trigger sufficient change. Whether that route is enough to deliver a more sustainable society is a question you will probably be asking yourself throughout the course and beyond.

One of the most attractive and simple things about the wedges approach is its optimistic but practical tone. Its authors note that the world has a very inefficient energy system – there is plenty of fat to cut. But the view of all the lit-up buildings and snakes of traffic from the top of a city-centre office block, or from a train window as it snakes through carbon-hungry suburbs, makes you wonder where change is going to come from. What evidence is there that leading professionals, businesspeople and governments are willing to help bring about dramatic changes for the better? What tools have they to break the problem down further into more manageable steps? The next section looks at an attempt to do precisely that in relation to making cities, towns and buildings more sustainable.

Translating sustainability: the example of One Planet Living

3

> The challenge that faces us all is: how can people everywhere enjoy a high quality of life, within the carrying capacity of one planet?
>
> *(BioRegional/WWF, 2008)*

According to the resources experts that have invented the term 'ecological footprint' (introduced in Part 3 Section 1), if everyone on Earth lived the high-consumption lifestyles of the average European, humanity would need three planets to live on. You will be familiar with the concept of an ecological footprint. It is a similar concept to a carbon footprint: indeed it is a way of converting carbon footprint into a land area and then adding in some other considerations, including biodiversity impacts. It is less precise, and hence open to criticism. But the key messages of this approach are simple: if all the humans on Earth were to live like the average American citizen, the figure in terms of land area required rises to roughly six planets. At the time of writing (2008) the average Chinese lifestyle requires just a little over one planet to sustain it, although that is set to change as more and more people in China, such as the Tans shown in *The Carbons and the Tans* video, pursue the comforts and pleasures of a Western way of life. The logic that sits behind the 'three planets' in Figure 4.11 is simple: the image demonstrates that it is essential that human societies find ways of living within their ecological means.

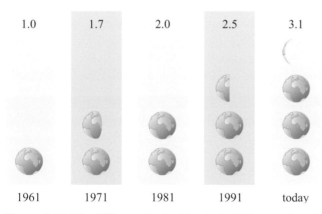

1.0	1.7	2.0	2.5	3.1
1961	1971	1981	1991	today

Figure 4.11 The UK's ecological footprint. The number of planets needed to support the whole world at UK levels of consumption has steadily increased. Thinking sustainably is in effect about trying to find ways of living within the means of the one planet that humans have to live on *(Source: Simms et al., 2007, Figure 7)*

This part will go on in the last sections to give concrete examples of how some of the 'wedges' can be delivered by the work of the designers, planners, policymakers and businesspeople who shape the nature of houses, towns and villages. Figure 4.12 shows how their work is particularly significant in terms of environmental impacts of human development. It will look at examples of how the concept of sustainability has been made to do practical work in the reshaping of the built environment. Figure 4.12 shows how cities, towns and buildings are responsible, directly or indirectly, for a very substantial share of the environmental impacts of human societies.

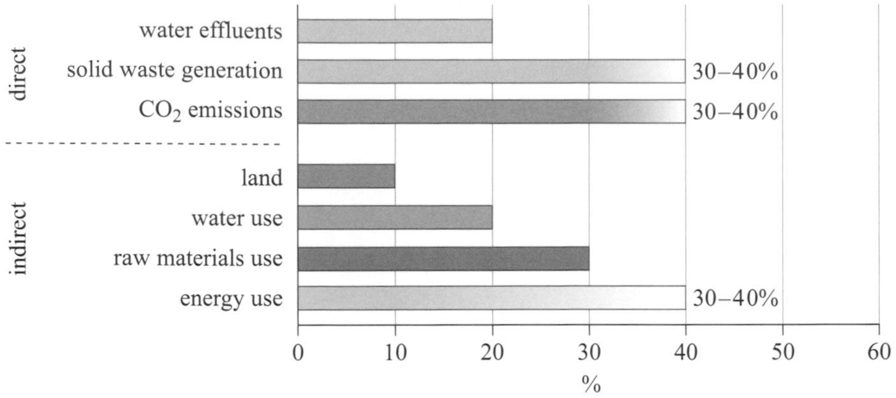

Figure 4.12 A very large portion of humanity's impact on the natural world can be traced back to the ways in which the built environment is designed and used
(Source: adapted from Tepe, 2007, Figure 1)

To help give some strategic direction to the professions, business and policy community that shape the built environment, the non-governmental organisation WWF International (also known as the Worldwide Fund for Nature) and a partner environmental body, BioRegional, developed the concept of One Planet Living™ (hereafter referred to as OPL). One of the important things about the concept is that it applies the principles of sustainability to one sector of the economy. However, where the wedges approach focuses on climate change, OPL encourages practitioners in government, business and professions to see their own work in terms of its sustainability. Through 'ten principles' the OPL approach gives a structured way of including concerns for biodiversity loss, water, air and soil quality and the health of the local economy and culture as well as climate change. Looking in some detail at the OPL concept (Box 4.3) allows you to explore one example of how environmentalists have engaged with the architects, planners, developers and construction industry to implement the principles of sustainability literally 'on the ground'.

Box 4.3   One Planet Living™ – why the trademark?

It is interesting that the partners felt it necessary to trademark their concept. There are probably two main reasons for this. The first is that they feel the need to protect the integrity of their approach to sustainability from any dilution or 'greenwash'. If unscrupulous developers wanted to bask in the 'green glow' of association with some of the terms associated with sustainable construction thinking without any real commitment to change, then there would be no progress towards sustainability. But the trademark also opens the way for the partners to secure a flow of funds from companies or projects that want to use the label as it gains wider legitimacy. This kind of mimicking of the behaviour of the corporate world within environmentalism is controversial with more radical environmentalists. The tension that results demonstrates that environmentalism is a broad movement, ranging from people who consider themselves 'realists', who are ready to do deals that promise some real day-to-day progress, through to radicals who want to press for more dramatic system-wide changes. There is a feeling amongst radical greens that moves such as to trademark a concept rooted in sustainability is to continue playing the game that has got humanity into such trouble.

There is an OPL programme aimed at helping individual households, following many of the approaches you will be familiar with from your reading of Part 3 of this block. However, the people behind this programme believe that the bigger steps towards a sustainable built environment are to be found in working at the level of big investment and planning decisions. Hence their aim is to work in partnership with developers, architects and planners to create more sustainable communities. It seems likely that their goal is not so much to see every development have an OPL stamp of approval, but rather to encourage high-profile demonstration projects that successfully show what can be achieved in terms of low environmental impact and high quality of life for inhabitants.

Appropriately, the head office of OPL is the first development of new buildings constructed with reference to their principles: the BedZED development in Surrey (see Figure 4.13). BedZED has enjoyed extensive media

(a)

(b)

(c)

Figure 4.13 BedZED, or Beddington Zero Energy Development to use its full name, is the first One Planet Living development, and home to their head office

coverage within the specialist construction press and in environmentalist circles. It is a good example of designers and builders looking at contemporary living 'in the round'. They haven't just looked at the technology or materials used in a specific building, but planned a whole community which aims to minimise energy, private transport and water use and maximise biological diversity and quality of life. In Figure 4.13 you can see some of these features. The colourful 'chimneys' or wind cowls are part of the 'passive' ventilation system; the 'green roofs' of sedum plants just underneath them help insulate the buildings and also attract insects and birds and reduce risk of flooding by holding water in heavy rains. The mix of timber, brick, and triple-glazed windows reflects a careful approach to putting the right material in the right place to maximise comfort and energy efficiency, as well as delivering an interesting-looking building that is durable and good to live and work in.

Much of the housing on the site is relatively high density (meaning a higher number of people living there than in an average suburban development) while still allowing people private space inside and out. This, along with other measures, reduces the need for private car ownership and is intended to encourage a stronger sense of community. It is a pioneering development, and has allowed many new technologies to be tested. As such, the designers acknowledge that not everything has gone to plan and, for example in terms of energy use, it did not initially achieve the reductions in carbon emissions it aimed for. Construction costs were also high for this innovative development. Nevertheless, the houses are a great deal cheaper to run and more resource-efficient than the norm, and the BedZED development has served its intended purpose of catalysing wider change. BedZED's design arose out of thinking systematically about the essential features of development based on the idea that there is just the one planet to live on. OPL honed in on ten key principles, based on ten global challenges. The OPL principles are expressed as specific goals and strategies in Figure 4.14.

Study note: ways of reading – scanning a piece of writing for 'sense'

Note that you may come across terms or phrases you are unfamiliar with. Don't get held up by these – perhaps make a note of them and check in the online glossary or a dictionary later. The main point is to get a sense quickly of the scope of the ten principles. Trying to grasp an overall impression of the key themes in a passage of writing without becoming weighed down by the detail is one of the skills you will develop as a student.

GLOBAL CHALLENGE	OPL PRINCIPLE	OPL GOAL and STRATEGY
Climate change due to human-induced build up of carbon dioxide (CO_2) in the atmosphere	Zero Carbon	*Achieve net CO_2 emissions of zero from OPL developments.* Implement energy efficiency in buildings and infrastructure; supply energy from on-site renewable sources, topped up by new off-site renewable supply where necessary.
Waste from discarded products and packaging create a huge disposal challenge while squandering valuable resources	Zero Waste	*Eliminate waste flows to landfill and for incineration* Reduce waste generation through improved design; encourage re-use, recycling and composting; generate energy from waste cleanly; eliminate the concept of waste as part of a resource-efficient society.
Travel by car and airplane can cause climate change, air and noise pollution, and congestion	Sustainable Transport	*Reduce reliance on private vehicles and achieve major reductions of CO_2 emissions from transport* Provide transport systems and infrastructure that reduce dependence on fossil fuel use, e.g., by cars and airplanes. Offset carbon emissions from air travel and perhaps car travel.
Destructive patterns of resource exploitation and use of non-local materials in construction and manufacture increase environmental harm and reduce gains to the local economy.	Local and Sustainable Materials	*Transform materials supply to the point where it has a net positive impact on the environment and local economy* Where possible, use local, reclaimed, renewable and recycled materials in construction and products, which minimises transport emissions, spurs investment in local natural resource stocks and boosts the local economy.
Industrial agriculture produces food of uncertain quality and harms local ecosystems, while consumption of non-local food imposes high-transport impacts	Local and Sustainable Food	*Transform food supply to the point where it has a net positive impact on the environment, local economy and peoples' well-being.* Support local and low impact food production that provides healthy, quality food while boosting the local economy in an environmentally beneficial manner; showcase examples, of low-impact packaging processing and disposal; highlight benefits of a low-impact diet.
Local supplies of freshwater are often insufficient to meet human needs due to pollution, disruption of hydrological cycles and depletion of existing stocks.	Sustainable Water	*Achieve a positive impact on local water resources and supply* Implement water use efficiency measure, re-use and recycling; minimise water extraction and pollution; foster sustainable water and sewage management in the landscape; restore natural water cycles.
Loss of biodiversity and habitats due to development in natural areas and over exploitation of natural resources	Natural Habitats and Wildlife	*Regenerate degraded environments and halt biodiversity loss* Protect or regenerate existing natural environments and the habitats they provide to fauna and flora; create new habitats.
Local cultural heritage is being lost throughout the world due to globalisation, resulting in a loss of local identity and wisdom	Culture and Heritage	*Protect and build on local cultural heritage and diversity* Celebrate and revive cultural heritage and the sense of local and regional identity; choose structures and systems that build on this heritage; foster a new culture of sustainability.
Some in the industrialised world live in relative poverty, while many in the developing world cannot meet their basic needs from what they produce or sell	Equity and Fair Trade	*Ensure that the OPL community's impact on other communities is positive* Promote equity and fair trading relationships to ensure the OPL community has a beneficial impact on other communities both locally and globally, notably disadvantaged communities.
Rising wealth and greater health and happiness increasingly diverge, raising questions about the true basis of well-being and contentment	Health and Happiness	*Increase health and quality of life of OPL community members and others* Promote healthy lifestyles and physical, mental and spiritual well-being through well-designed structures and community engagement measures, as well as by delivering on social and environmental targets.

Figure 4.14 The ten OPL principles *(Source: BioRegional/WWF, 2008)*

Activity 4.3   OPL principles – what are quantitative and qualitative measures?

Some of the OPL principles can be measured in terms of numbers (quantitative), whereas others are much more the result of judgement and wider analysis (qualitative). Pick out two or three that can be easily measured against a quantitative (number) target and separately note down some of those that are more qualitative (about a judgement).

Discussion

Carbon dioxide emissions or waste targets can be expressed as numbers, and it will be possible to compare the performance of an OPL development against those of 'standard' developments (although of course the goal of the OPL's originators is to make targets similar to theirs the standard). Some principles, however, are about judgement and debate, where language counts for more than numbers in summarising progress. It is difficult to find a single indicator of health and happiness, of cultural health and diversity or to express how a community promotes fairness, although some have tried. There are government-published sets of 'sustainable development indicators' as well as experiments with single indicators that take into account ecological and social welfare as well as economic indicators. Just as the making of this course required collaboration and innovation by partners from a range of disciplinary backgrounds, this activity is a reminder that assessing progress towards sustainability requires an interdisciplinary approach that brings together qualitative and quantitative information.

With many of the principles it isn't too difficult to see how the people who shape a new housing development can promote some of these principles. The next section will introduce some examples of buildings that seek to address the same set of concerns. But the cases considered also point to some of the tensions, ambiguities and even contradictions that can arise when trying to build in a more sustainable manner. Aiming to use local materials in construction can be made an integral part of new projects, but they might be more energy intensive than an alternative. It might be possible to supply a niche sustainable buildings market in the present with locally sourced timber, but a large expansion in demand might introduce less sustainable local forestry practices.

It can also be difficult to see how pursuit of goals such as 'local and sustainable food', 'culture and heritage', 'equity and Fair Trade' or 'health and happiness' can be integrated into construction industry decision making. The architects, engineers and planners tend to have to prioritise the business of putting up buildings on time and to an agreed price. Hence they might be able to integrate features that keep the energy bill down, but are not motivated to think in terms of how a building fits into a city's food system, or the local wages of cleaning staff, or cultural and heritage concerns.

Yet the OPL approach is an example of trying to communicate to the construction sector that sustainability thinking is about approaching both problems and solutions in terms of interconnected wholes. Hence, just as most 1960s and 1970s town planning and housing developments were designed around assumptions about cheap energy and universal car ownership, the leading thinking in terms of sustainable building aims to massively reduce energy consumption and eliminate the need for private road transport. To do that will require the creation not just of low-impact buildings, but whole communities where people's need and desire to travel has been greatly reduced. Many aspects of their daily lives, including how they shop and eat and how they spend their leisure time, need to be considered relevant to how cities develop. The next few years will see more examples of trying to put these principles into practice, such as One Gallions in East London (see Figure 4.15). These are not simply developed world challenges: fast growing Brazilian and Chinese cities will also have to meet the needs and aspirations of people while still living within the means of the one planet Earth.

Figure 4.15 There are plenty of ambitious ideas, like this flagship eco-development for the Thames Gateway, One Gallions, that has been designed around the OPL principles, but how will they work if and when they come off the drawing board? It is an important story you may wish to follow

One of the more serious charges against all of the concepts you have looked at in this part – carbon reductions wedges and One Planet Living – is that they read well enough stuck to a drawing board, but is it possible for designers, architects, planners and developers to transform the thinking behind every single new building that comes into being? The 'wedges' approach and OPL concept both seek to break the broad concept of sustainability into manageable menus of actions and considerations. They don't claim to be complete solutions in themselves, but rather experiments in making workable communications and decision-making tools. So much for the theory: what is sustainable building in practice? It is helpful now to look at existing examples of building projects that lay claim to being far more sustainable than the norm.

4   Building sustainability

The prefix *eco* was discussed in Part 2 of this block. In the Greek it refers to 'household' and it is a common root for the words ecology and economy. It is a central insight for anyone seeking to understand environmental change problems and solutions to recognise that planet Earth is the household both for humanity and for all life on Earth. It is only a short intellectual step to acknowledge that the wider community of life on Earth is vital to human survival. This is really just another way of saying that all economic development must be sustainable.

The cases discussed in this section are also illustrated in a 12-minute video entitled Building towards sustainability that you can view at any time before, during or after reading this material. The video helps to give context to the discussion, and allows you to get to know some of the people involved in the projects and get a better picture of the buildings.

4.1 Building Eden

Such insights have nourished new approaches in architectural design, construction and use of buildings. A good place to start looking for examples is the Eden Project in Cornwall. The Eden Project is a centre for inspirational learning about environmental change problems and solutions, based around a 'world garden'. Recalling from Part 2 of this block that sustainability aims to be about bringing together the social, ecological and economic spheres, it is apt that the site is a disused clay pit in what was an economically depressed part of Cornwall. It has brought new jobs and visitors but

Figure 4.16 A sunflower, the inspiration for the Eden Project's Core Education Centre

has also regenerated the area's biological diversity. In terms of the buildings on the site it has sought to set new standards for the sustainability of the construction, use and (eventual) disposal of its buildings.

To illustrate their approach, this section spends time looking at the design, construction and use of Eden's education centre, the Core. The building aims to express the Eden Project's values in every respect. This includes its design, the materials used and their durability, its consumption of natural resources, the environmental costs of the building through the course of its life, and the experience of visitors. The architects wanted the simple, everyday experience of walking into the space, with its numerous supporting 'trunks' of laminated timber beams and overhead 'canopy' roof, to provoke thinking about people's place in their natural world.

Figure 4.17 The Eden Project's Core Education Centre. The aim was to 'create a building the shape of a sunflower and size of a spaceship to pay respect to the plant engine that powers the Earth'.

Design is a complex process, with a very large number of considerations to bear in mind. In order to engage with the thinking behind this building, this section focuses largely on the roof structure of the Core. It looks specifically at the selection of a material that would give it a waterproof 'skin'. The roof as a whole is intended to achieve much more than keeping the weather out. Through its solar photovoltaic panels it generates electricity (estimated at 20 000 kilowatt hours per year, saving over 9 tonnes of CO_2 annually). With plentiful natural lighting (including the use of mirrors) and very high levels of insulation (made from recycled newspapers) the demand for energy for a building of this scale is dramatically reduced. It also acts as a reservoir by collecting rainwater that is stored for use in the building's toilets.

At the same time its design also seeks to communicate some fundamental messages about the highly efficient patterns that are found in the plant world. Both the designers of the roof, and Peter Randall-Page, the sculptor of the granite 'seed' sculpture that sits at the core of The Core, are fascinated by the economy of the plant world. That is, they are intrigued by the tendency in plant structures to evolve to the most efficient forms. A particular form that occurs in many plants, including most visibly in sunflowers (Figure 4.16) and pine cones is that of opposing spirals (see Figures 4.18 and 4.19). These allow growth from a central point in such a way that serves to maximise surface area (in the case of the sunflower this increases the area available for pollination).

Figure 4.18 Images of the 'seed' sculpture by Peter Randall-Page that sits at the centre of the Core building and expresses what he describes as 'one of nature's great superstructures'. This is because it allows growth from a central point while maximising surface area.

Figure 4.19 In the words of one of the architects, Jolyon Brewis: 'We decided that the structure of the building itself should be derived from the double spiral, and we looked to the mathematics behind these spirals in nature to generate the design. We were delighted to discover that this produced an efficient and elegant network of timber beams.' The roof structure also serves as a mini power station and water collector.

Careful choices based on good information can help reduce environmental impacts for the long term. To meet environmental sustainability criteria, a design and construction team needs information on the impacts of the materials they specify in terms of the total environmental impacts of their extraction (e.g. for forestry or mining), of their processing, shipping and installation, and of their performance and durability in use. To meet social sustainability criteria, building professionals will also need to be aware of the social consequences of particular product choices. For example, they will need to ask themselves: 'What are the impacts on distant communities of my decision to choose that timber floor that is sourced from Indonesia, or that kind of metal that is mined in southern Africa?'

They will also need to consider what the future of the materials will be when they come to the end of their useful life on the roof. This 'cradle to grave' approach is called *life cycle assessment* (LCA), sometimes known as life-cycle analysis (recall that this was mentioned in Parts 1 and 3). This is a very demanding mix of criteria to meet. They established that the underlying structure of the building would be made from timber laminated 'glulam' beams. These are a fairly recent technological development where timber planks are glued together to create beams that can have the strength of steel but a lower environmental impact. This lower impact derives from the fact that, with sustainable forestry practices, timber is a renewable resource, while steel is energy intensive to produce.

The design team needed to identify an effective thin 'skin' that would protect this structure from the elements. In what is effectively a demonstration project the Core's design team were looking for a range of properties in their roofing materials. They wanted them to:

- make a strong architectural statement and nourish the reputation for innovative buildings on the site
- be long-lasting, strong and fairly light
- be easy to work, given the complexity of the roof design

and they wanted to:

- be able to trace the environmental and social impacts of the specified materials.

The case study below charts their decision to specify copper (see Figure 4.20). This could be considered a controversial choice. Copper is energy intensive in manufacture, and often mined very remotely from where it is used (see Figure 4.21). The mining industry also has a long history of pollution and habitat destruction. It is worth following their thinking in some detail.

Figure 4.20 The Eden Project's Core education building's roof has a thin skin of copper. This controversial choice was made in part because the design team wanted to promote more sustainable mining and construction.

The Core's copper skin 'from rock to roof': a controversial choice?

After considering a range of options the team began researching metal roofing and became convinced that not only might copper provide a good architectural solution, but it could offer a way of setting new sustainability standards within the mining industry. Many environmentalists would consider the decision to work with the mining industry controversial: mining has been associated with poor environmental and social standards, and mined metals are by definition non-renewable resources.

However, the Eden Project and their partners had been in dialogue with the mining industry on sustainability issues in the past, and it was felt that collaboration on the roof was a sensible development upon that work. The collaboration reflects a view of the project as a whole that they want to engage the 'mainstream' of society in sustainability thinking.

The OPL principles argue for local materials – but copper is the opposite. However, the principles also make reference to local culture and heritage, hence it is no accident that the Eden Project took such an interest in mining and metals. Mining has a central role in Cornwall's economic and social history; indeed, the Eden Project is sited in an exhausted china-clay quarry. Hence the project wanted to use their power as prominent building clients to push for higher standards in the industry.

Several metals were considered and the team settled on copper as the option that was closest to fitting their demanding brief. They could have specified recycled copper but that was felt to be the easy route. It would have pacified environmental critics, but there would not have been any opportunity to provoke new thinking within the mining industry. They decided to use their influence as clients on a high-profile project to try to promote more sustainable supply chains within the minerals sector.

One of the things that provoked their choice was that there was far less analysis and information available compared with specifying timber. The supply chain for timber products has seen the development of a number of labelling schemes – perhaps best known being the Forest Stewardship Council's (FSC) scheme. But no equivalent existed that assessed the sustainability of the metals mining and production supply chain. The FSC scheme is an example of *supply chain certification*. Such certifications for forest, fisheries and Fair Trade products are now well established; however, it has been much rarer for an end user to show interest in the supply chain of mined products.

Hence their specification of a copper roof was aimed at promoting new thinking about certification standards in the mining industry. The supply chain analysis that follows the copper's story 'from rock to roof' is shown in cartoon form in Figure 4.21.

SAQ 4.2   What were the pros and cons in choosing a copper 'skin' on the Core roof?

Drawing on the case study, including the video material on the DVD, and paragraphs that precede it, identify three reasons why the choice of a copper skin on the Core roof could be considered controversial. Also identify three reasons why, on balance, the design team chose copper for this purpose.

The team's conclusions about the extensive work on trying to promote sustainability thinking in the mining industry show that sustainable decision making is complex and fraught with technical challenges and conflicts. They concluded that '[f]rom this exercise it was apparent that there is no definitive prescriptive mechanism for determining what is the most sustainable material' (Eden Centre, n.d.). Nevertheless, they feel confident that the work has encouraged much more reflection on sustainability concerns and LCA within the mining industry. So, just as with the wedges and the OPL concepts, this is another example of how sustainability is not so much a matter of following agreed rules as of thinking through processes critically in any given situation. It is about trade-offs. The quality of information, and the level of commitment to finding new ways of doing things, will dictate whether more sustainable outcomes are achieved.

SAQ 4.3   Criteria for sustainable construction

Your knowledge of sustainability concerns and the OPL principles make it possible for you to summarise the kinds of question that a meeting of architect, surveyor and supplier should ask when preparing to build to high sustainability criteria. List up to five of the questions you would want such a meeting to address.

The Eden Project team have set out to be pioneers, but this is hardly surprising: they are under very close scrutiny concerning their environmental performance by the media and public. The Core can afford an exceptionally high investment in human resources in terms of research and project management. While such a one-off project generates some valuable learning, it is more important that there are also pioneers working to meet more mundane but significant demands for housing and workplaces. Two examples of this can be found on a much smaller scale just a few miles from the Eden Project.

Figure 4.21 The Eden Project chose to engage with the mining industry directly in order to encourage more sustainable practices in that sector. Their cartoon describing the process shows how many places and parties are involved in the mining and manufacturing process (*Source: Eden project n.d.*)

① Blasting

The Bingham Canyon ore contains just 0.6% copper. To extract it from the ground groups of holes 10–20 metres deep are drilled and filled with half a tonne of explosives.

② Crushing

The blasted rock is trucked to a 'crusher' in the pit – 136,000 tonnes of ore per day are crushed to chunks less than 25 cm in diameter.

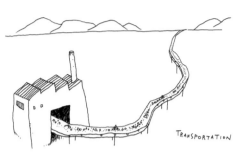

③ Transporting

The ore is moved from the mine to the 'concentrator' by five miles of conveyor belts. At the concentrator the ore is crushed and ground to the consistency of face talcum powder.

④ Flotation

The powder is passed through a series of flotations where chemicals and liquids are applied to separate the minerals from ground ore. The concentrate produced by flotation contains about 28% copper.

⑤ Smelting

The concentration is then pumped as a slurry 17 miles to the smelter where it is dried, then melted so it can be separated into gases (particularly sulphur oxides); slag (mostly silica and iron) and copper matte, which is 70% copper.

⑥ Anode casting

The copper matte is melted again to remove more impurities and the molten liquid is cast into anodes at 99.6% copper. The anodes are taken to the 'refinery' where the remaining impurities are removed, forming a plate of 99.99% copper.

⑦ Transport of cathodes

The cathodes are strapped together in 8-tonne bundles, loaded on to trains and ships for customers around the world. In our case, they went to the fabricator, KME in Germany.

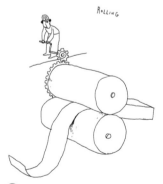

⑧ Rolling

At the fabricator, the copper is melted yet again and put through a series of rollers to form wire, tubes and sheets.

⑨ Our roof

Copper sheets were transported in rolls to Eden, cut to shape, and installed on our roof by Richardson's Roofing Ltd.

4.2 Pioneer builders

Tim Stirrup (Figure 4.22) is an example of someone who has shown the same commitment to ecological principles as the Eden Project, but on a more modest scale. As a joiner and builder he was looking for a site for his own business when he came across some derelict farm buildings. After a great deal of research and work, Tim's company created the Mount Pleasant Ecological Park of rural industrial units, shown in Figure 4.23 and in the video on the course DVD.

Some of the features integrated into the building include:

- The largest load-bearing rammed earth wall in the UK. The use of the soil that was on site greatly reduced emissions associated with specifying and transporting energy-intensive concrete products.
- Roof tiles made from recycled rubber tyres – hence reducing landfill and environmental costs of new slate production.
- Rainwater collected from the roof to supply the toilets.
- Solar panels used to heat the water for the bathrooms.
- Heating system powered by waste from the timber-based building business.
- Installation of high-efficiency lighting and appliances to keep electricity demand down.

Figure 4.22 Tim Stirrup of Pioneer Environmental Building, working to take the principles of sustainability off the drawing board and into everyday projects

The Ecological Park is an inspiring example, and the work of a few environmentally committed builders is important in demonstrating what can be done: it gives 'green consumers' a choice and it can inspire some others to follow their lead. It is worth saying that many of the less conventional choices will stay that way: the rammed earth technique used in the floors and walls will work only where the earth has particular properties, and it is labour intensive. Tim Stirrup found the costs of this choice were

(a)

(b)

(c)

(d)

Figure 4.23 Mount Pleasant Ecological Park: (a) welcome sign; (b) the park is home to a mix of local businesses. At first glance these rural industrial units look much like any other. Closer inspection reveals a host of features that have dramatically reduced the environmental impacts of the buildings, and offered comfort, affordability and attractiveness; **(c) the floor is made of rammed earth taken from the site on which the building stands, polished to give a cheap, hard-wearing finish with a beautifully rich colour; (d) the walls are also made of rammed earth.** The use of local earth reduces transport impacts of 'imported' materials, and the construction method results in very low carbon emissions.

approximately the same as a conventional concrete specification, but the considerations would differ at another site, and point to another solution.

The point of these cases is not to hold up the particular techniques or choices as universal paths to follow, but rather to indicate underlying ways of thinking about materials and the life and use of a building. For these ways of thinking to be made mainstream across the building industry it will be necessary to develop solutions that can be easily scaled up.

One way of catalysing change and sharing best practice is to run architectural competitions. Much of the thinking about sustainable building focuses on cities and doesn't address the needs of more rural areas. Hence the

Cornwall Sustainable Building Trust ran a competition that invited architects to design a zero-emission house that answered the needs of the UK's South West, a region with a shortage of affordable rural homes. Paul Bright, the trust's chief executive, explained the reasons for the competition thus: 'The objective was to show we could make house-building totally sustainable. There should be no need to [waste] energy by importing raw materials from the other side of the world, or transporting skilled labour from the rest of Britain' (Norwood, 2005).

The winning design was a proposal for carbon-neutral timber kit homes, called the RuralZED (pictured in Figure 4.24). The 'ZED' in the title refers to Zero Emission Development and is a piece of jargon first developed in relation to new-built urban developments such as BedZED – the Beddington ZED in Surrey that was pictured in Figure 4.13 above. The RuralZED was again developed with reference to the OPL principles, and designed by the same architectural practice. Sustainable building faces even more challenges in rural areas (including increased costs and planning restrictions), and there are serious problems facing rural communities in terms of affordability and availability of housing. The environmental considerations also differ in some ways. The designer's role is key in addressing these challenges. The ZED architectural practice have developed a housing

Figure 4.24 The RuralZED brings together research into more sustainable services technologies (heating, cooling, water, light) and architectural knowledge of low-impact building into one design that meets the distinctive housing needs of rural areas. Concrete panels set in the timber frame provide thermal mass.

design that promises affordable, potentially self-built, homes that can be constructed using mostly locally sourced materials. By reviewing all the obstacles to the provision of more sustainable buildings in a systematic fashion, they hope they have developed one means of helping to make sustainable construction the everyday norm. Although initially designed for a rural context, they do believe it to be relevant to suburban and urban settings too.

The kit design is intended to make it easier to gain planning consents by anticipating potential planning system obstacles. It is also meant to make the specifying of materials and technologies more straightforward. This is just one example of attempts in the building industry to make more sustainable choices in design and construction more cost effective and easily achieved within the industry. Although the ZED factory are a prominent example, they are simply one example of attempts to 'scale up' sustainable design from expensive-one off projects to whole developments. One interesting detail is that one of the conditions of purchase of a RuralZED licence as a builder is attendance on a training course (see Figure 4.25). This recognises that it is not just the technology and design, but also the construction process that requires new ways of thinking.

Figure 4.25 Training will be essential in raising capacity to deliver more sustainable buildings. This shows trainees building the prototype RuralZED house in Cornwall.

This section has sought to show that making progress towards sustainable building is possible, and that there are examples of pioneering projects. These projects also show that there is not a definitive last word on what is or isn't sustainable, but rather a continuous process of experiment and learning. The key to progress lies in constantly keeping in mind the underlying (admittedly fluid) principles of sustainability and asking questions of all products or processes. But the most significant opportunities to 'scale up' the application of more sustainable building principles lies in the hands of governments.

5 Building policies that face the future

One missing piece that hasn't been discussed up to now is the role of policy in shaping the decisions of architects, planners, builders and suppliers. The creativity and determination displayed by some of the pioneering examples in Section 4 will remain interesting exceptions without a clear policy framework. Government policies need to find ways of rewarding sustainable building practices and deterring the energy-wasting, non-ecological norm. Pressures for more housing are intense in the UK. For claims about sustainable new building to stand up there is a very varied set of demands to be answered – ecological, social and economic. In practice this is proving controversial: the Thames Gateway developments (see Figure 4.26) will be under close scrutiny from different interests. What can policy do to integrate these varied demands? British policymakers are optimistic. They hope that a new framework of standards and assessments for housing development will result in a dramatic reduction in the environmental impact of house building within just a few years.

Figure 4.26 Model including the proposed Thames Gateway development, shown at the 2008 Ecobuild show in London

The UK government has used both carrots and sticks in promoting more sustainable building. That is, it has applied both voluntary codes and stringent regulations in the pursuit of an ambitious target it set in 2007 for all new homes in England and Wales to be 'zero carbon' by 2016 (see Box 4.4). 'The Code for Sustainable Homes was introduced to improve the overall sustainability of new homes by setting a single national standard within which the home building industry can design and construct homes to higher environmental standards and offers a tool for developers to differentiate themselves within the market' (Department for Communities and Local Government, 2008, p. 4). In the words of a UK government policy document it aims to achieve the zero carbon goal in three steps: 'moving first, in 2010 to a 25 per cent improvement in the energy/carbon performance set in the 2006 Building Regulations; then second, in 2013, to a 44 per cent improvement; then, finally in 2016, to zero carbon ... (Z)ero carbon means that, over a year, the net carbon emissions from all energy use in the home would be zero.' (Department for Communities and Local Government, 2007, p. 4)

In the same period the government announced plans for a series of eco-towns, that is, developments that would encourage designers and construction companies to accelerate the shift towards a zero carbon built environment. The government argued that '[e]co-towns offer the opportunity to achieve high standards of sustainable living while also maximising the potential for affordable housing.' (info4local.co.uk, n.d.). The eco-towns proposals have proven controversial and demonstrated the range of opinion within the environmental movement. Some support government plans, attracted by the idea of focusing design and planning skills on some leading-edge examples. Others have dismissed the plans as 'greenwash' intended to get around planning laws, or distract attention from wider plans that will destroy rural land to create new suburban housing (Figure 4.27).

Figure 4.27 Protests against proposed 'eco-towns' have again shown that 'sustainability' is a contested and fluid term: it can mean very different things to different people

Here is an extended quote from the policy document *Building for a Sustainable Future*, a policy document that explains the UK government's justification for changes in housing standards towards the zero carbon goal, and their plans for implementation. You will work with this quote in Activity 4.4.

> Emissions of greenhouse gases, particularly carbon dioxide, are the main cause of climate change. The UK emitted more than 550 million tonnes of carbon dioxide ($MtCO_2$) in 2005. Energy use in buildings accounted for nearly half these emissions, and more than a quarter came from the energy we use to heat, light and run our homes.
>
> Energy security is also an important challenge. We became a net importer of oil in 2006, and are dependent on imported gas at a time when global demand and prices are increasing. Many of the measures needed to cut carbon emissions to address climate change also contribute to creating a healthy diversity of energy supply, and address fuel poverty through lower bills for householders.
>
> Against this backdrop, we need to address the issue of housing supply. Evidence indicates that too few homes have been built to meet demand over the last three decades of the 20th century. As [the] report into housing supply made clear, we need additional housing provision ... If we do not increase house building above previous plans, the percentage of 30–34 year old couples able to afford to buy will worsen significantly in the long term, falling from over half today to around 35 per cent in 2026.
>
> If we build the houses we need, then by 2050, as much as one-third of the total housing stock will have been built between now and then. So we need to build in a way that helps our strategy to cut carbon emissions – both through reducing emissions of new homes and by changing technology and the markets so as to cut emissions from existing homes too. We want to see a volume of new development which will deliver economies of scale and bring down costs of environmental technologies that could apply not only to new homes but to existing homes too.
>
> *(Department for Communities and Local Government, 2008, p. 4)*

Box 4.4   How do you define a zero carbon development?

Zero carbon, the goal of the UK government's target for new housing in England and Wales for 2016 (and all buildings by 2019), seems to be an immediately intuitive and good idea. A similar phrase is 'zero energy development' or zero emissions development (the ZED Factory architectural practice mentioned above took their name from this phrase). In Germany policymakers have developed the *Passivhaus* standard to clarify the situation (see Figure 4.28). But a pause for thought raises the question – what do these terms actually mean in practice? Should it include the energy used in transporting materials to the site? Does it allow energy from renewables such as wind turbines that is not generated at or near to the building or building development? A consultant's report for the Regional Development Agency for the South West (the region that the cases considered in Section 4 come from) tried to clear up this confusion. They defined zero carbon development as 'development that delivers zero net emissions (over the course of a year) of carbon dioxide into the atmosphere resulting from energy use in buildings. This definition therefore excludes energy used for transport and embodied energy in materials.' (oursouthwest, n.d.). At the time of writing it also seems to exclude using electricity generated by remote renewables such as offshore wind farms (or by nuclear power) but this is still to be resolved.

For a policy to be effective the definitions of terms used need to be watertight. The combination of fast-evolving technologies and policies, and public opinion that is mistrustful of 'greenwash' claims, mean that any industry will need to be careful to 'show its working' to its partners, government (national and local) and the public.

Figure 4.28 A development in Freiburg built to some of the highest environmental standards in Europe, known as the *Passivhaus* standard. The project combined refurbishment and new-build in pursuit of a sustainable community.

Study note: references and sources in academic writing

The extended quote that appears here offers a good opportunity to make a few points about how to quote from texts in your own work. In the case of short quotes, these can be embedded in the text in quote marks. You will have seen examples of this earlier in the block. Larger quotes, like the one here, appear in a different style, clearly indicating the beginning and end of the quote. In either case, to allow a reader to go to the original source I have clearly indicated both the author of the quote and a year. I have also included a page number wherever possible. This makes for a more authoritative document that clearly demonstrates the careful research I have done. In a paper in an academically refereed journal there could be hundreds of references in a piece of writing shorter than this part of the course. There are a number of different ways of referencing, but if you wanted to refer to what you've just read in this paragraph in another piece of work, such as an essay or report, there is a good chance you will use what is known as the 'Harvard method' or author–date referencing. For the Harvard method of referencing, you would simply put the family name, year and, if you have taken a direct quote or specific idea, the page number. For example, I might refer to a particular idea on a particular page in my last book, and I would point the reader to precisely that page at the end of the sentence (Smith, 2005, p. 23). At the end of the essay you would then list all the references alphabetically, including the name of the publisher and their location, for example:

author(s)   title   place of publication

Smith, J. (2005) *What do Greens Believe?* London, Granta

date of publication   publisher

Because it is published by a government department rather than an individual, the full reference for the long quote above would read:

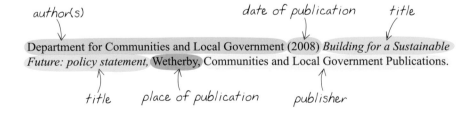

212

You will sometimes see writers referring to secondary sources and primary sources. If you were doing an English literature course then a textbook or commentary about a Shakespeare play would be a secondary source, and the original play *The Tempest*, for example, would be a primary source. This block is a secondary source, built up through the authors' reading and note taking based on both secondary and primary sources. In analysing written material a reader gives different kinds of 'weight' or authority to different kinds of text. Use of a well-regarded primary source, or a reputable secondary source that clearly references the roots of its own arguments and data, will add to the authority and trustworthiness of a piece of writing. As a higher education student you will be expected to recognise and acknowledge the nature and relative authority of the different sources you might be using.

Activity 4.4   Taking notes from the policy document
Building for a Sustainable Future

Read through the quote again carefully. The passage gives a clear explanation of the justification for policy. Take no more than 10 minutes to 'translate' this passage into a number of points. Identify the main points (about six) and list them. The main points are the essential things the author is trying to communicate.

Discussion

I translated the passage into the following bullet points, cutting the number of words from more than 400 to fewer than 90, and resulting in a form that is easier to refer to.

- Climate science, despite uncertainties, justifies action.

- Energy use in buildings generates, or is related to, up to half of UK CO_2 emissions (the main cause of climate change).

- Sustainable building can cut carbon emissions, improve energy security and help address fuel poverty.

- Research shows unmet demand for affordable new homes.

- New development can bring economies of scale and accelerate introduction of new environmental technologies for both existing and new homes.

I have listed what I see as the main points by summarising each paragraph as a bullet point. Your list is going to be slightly different from mine. Note that there are other forms of note-taking technique, such as spray diagrams, that you will become familiar with during this course.

Just as a building is a complex thing, so is the network of policies, professions, market conditions and businesses that shape the outcomes of the construction process. The EU, national and local government, and the range of relevant interests (architecture, planning, construction industries, services) and their professional bodies all have an influence. Most of their roles in the building process evolved in a period when fossil fuels were cheap and local issues such as air and water quality or global issues such as climate change were generally unrecognised. The construction industry has a long journey ahead if it is to make progress towards sustainability.

Government regulations and minimum standards can be effective in some areas, for example specifying more demanding levels of insulation and banning some forms of wasteful appliance (e.g. through lighting, heating system and appliance standards). The state can also set the wider atmosphere for technological and professional development and product choice through a mix of taxes and benefits (such as grants) that reward efficiency and punish wasteful use of resources. In other areas government will need to work with other partners, including industry and higher education. Training is one such area – whether for architects and planners or plumbers and electricians. The state can wield a mix of carrots and sticks that set the atmosphere within which building professionals work. In these ways policies change the practices of the whole industry, but the related professions and industries and research and teaching communities also have key roles to play.

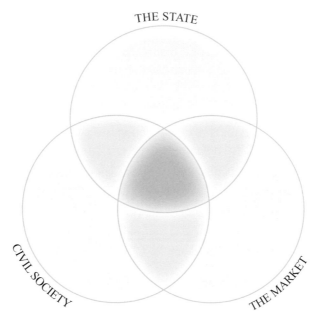

Figure 4.29 Venn diagram illustrating state, market and civil society

SAQ 4.4   Who is responsible for advancing sustainable construction?

Try to place each of the eight actions listed below somewhere in the Venn diagram. You could write them as short notes within the diagram, or, given that space is limited, you may just want to use the numbers. Which, for example, fall wholly in 'state'? Do any fall into both 'market' and 'civil society'? Are there any that fall into all three? Doing this will help to underline both the wide division of responsibilities and the reality of what the often-heard rhetoric of 'partnerships' in promoting sustainability really means. Is there a particular sphere where you feel that most responsibility falls? When you have done that, write a sentence or two that considers why those actions that fall within more than one circle of the Venn diagram can be the most difficult to assign responsibility for or to progress actions on.

1   Increase the cost of fossil fuel energy (expressed in costs of lighting, heating, building materials, transport).

2   Raise the capacity of construction trades (e.g. plumbers', electricians', joiners' training) to use sustainable products and practices.

3   Promote ideas for better quality of life in cities.

4   Retrofit existing housing with high levels of insulation and more efficient heating equipment.

5   Install insulation and more efficient heating equipment into newly built housing.

6   Make demands for more sustainable technologies and products.

7   Meet demand for more sustainable technologies and products.

8   Campaign for rapid action from business and government.

The Lighthouse demonstration project that appears in Figures 4.30 and 4.31 was, at the time of construction, thought to be one of the most sustainable houses in the UK. It was not an expensive one-off house for a wealthy 'eco-chic' client, but was designed and built by one of the country's major building products companies with affordable high-volume production in mind. One of the things that the building seeks to demonstrate is that sustainable design could result in a significant improvement in quality of life. The level of progress that housebuilders make towards zero carbon development in coming years will be a key indicator of global capacity to take the challenge of sustainability seriously.

Figure 4.30 The highly efficient 'Lighthouse' was sponsored by the building products supplier Kingspan in 2008 as a demonstration zero carbon project at the Building Research Establishment. At the time it was widely recognised as one of the most sustainable houses in Britain

Figure 4.31 One of the most interesting things about the Lighthouse is that it is clearly a strong contemporary design, and suggests that sustainable living can result in an improved quality of life – rather than a threat to it

Summary of Part 4

Part 4 has gone beyond individual and community 'grassroots' efforts to consider the roles and responsibilities of government, industry and professions in accelerating shifts towards sustainable development. It has sought to provoke thinking about the issues involved in a 'scaling up' of the ideas identified in reducing the carbon footprint of a household in Part 3 to new building projects. It has expanded on the notion of slices or wedges of carbon emissions reduction that you considered in *The Carbons and Pacala's wedges* video, allowing you to get a sense of the kinds of technical, policy and behavioural changes that might deliver substantial emissions reductions. It also introduced a conceptual tool that is being promoted as a way of progressing sustainability in the field of construction, the One Planet Living principles. Section 4 considered some specific examples of leading-edge building projects that are more sustainable in their design features, construction and use, and the final section introduced the kinds of policy changes that are likely to be needed to accelerate the shift to a more sustainable society in the construction sector.

After completing Part 4 you should be able to:

1 identify the relative roles of individuals, states, markets and the institutions of civil society in influencing attitudes towards sustainability

2 recognise that there is a range of opinions on how human societies might respond to environmental change

3 explore the role that communications and decision-making tools play in facilitating action on environmental change at a structural and institutional scale

4 describe case studies that demonstrate more sustainable building practices

5 take notes using bullet points, understand the difference between primary and secondary texts, and follow good practice in referencing texts.

This first block of the course has introduced you to the importance of rooting discussion of environmental change in the best available scientific knowledge. But it has also demonstrated that environmental issues raise many political, ethical and social questions. It has also shown how changing behaviour and different technology choices can greatly reduce environmental impact, whether at the level of the individual, a household or a city, and enable progress towards a more sustainable society.

Answers to SAQs

SAQ 4.1

1   1 billion tonnes carbon (or 3.7 billion tonnes CO_2) per year.

2   14 billion tonnes carbon (or 52 billion tonnes CO_2) per year.

SAQ 4.2

Several aspects of the decision to specify copper could be considered controversial:

1   Choosing a metal me ant working with an industry with a history of negative environmental and social impacts.

2   Having chosen copper, the design team did not use recycled but rather newly mined copper.

3   The copper was far from local – it made a long journey to the site, and its processing and transport would have implied significant carbon emissions.

However, the design team felt that these factors were outweighed by the benefits:

1   It offered a good solution in terms of providing an easily worked, light, long-lasting and waterproof skin.

2   It allowed the Eden Project to pilot a life cycle assessment/certification approach within the mining sector.

3   The association with mining had strong cultural and economic resonance with Cornwall.

SAQ 4.3

This is by no means a conclusive list, but a full answer is likely to include the following points:

• Where have the raw materials come from and what are the social and environmental impacts of their extraction in that location?

• What are the carbon emissions and other environmental impacts associated with choosing a particular material?

• How durable are the materials: will they provide a roof with a 60-year lifespan or will it need replacing or substantial repair work much earlier than then?

• What will happen at the end of its life as a roof? Will it be reusable or recyclable, or can its components be broken down into useful waste products (e.g. frame timbers used as a fuel source or insulation as a compostable material)?

• How well can the chosen material support other sustainable design features, e.g. renewable energy technologies or water collection?

• Does it support or easily allow natural day-lighting and air conditioning?

• Is the design engaging and inspiring? Does it contribute to the quality of the built environment?

SAQ 4.4

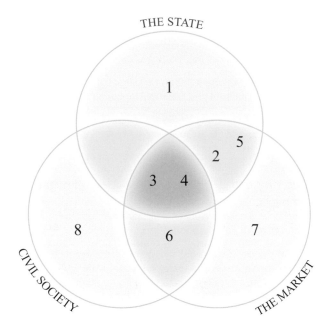

Figure 4.32 Completed Venn diagram

Those actions that fall into more than one category suggest that responsibility is divided between more than just the 'the state', 'the market' or 'civil society'. These are often the actions where the division of responsibility makes accountability more difficult to assign and action more difficult to progress. As a result, opinion can differ as to where responsibilities lie.

References

BioRegional/WWF (2008), *The Principles of One Planet Living*, http://www.panda.org/about_wwf/what_we_do/policy/one_planet_living/about_opl/principles/index.cfm (Accessed 5 August 2008).

Department for Communities and Local Government (2008) *Building for a Sustainable Future: policy statement*, Wetherby, Communities and Local Government Publications.

Department for Communities and Local Government (2007) *Building a Greener Future: policy statement*, Wetherby, Communities and Local Government Publications.

The Eden Centre (n.d.) *From Rock to Roof*, www.edenproject.com/documents/rocktoroof.pdf (Accessed 24 September 2008).

The Eden project (n.d.) *The Jounery of a Roof*, p. 21.

Info4local.gov.uk (n.d.) *The Code for Sustainable Homes*, www.info4local.gov.uk/content-by-topic/the-code (Accessed 24 September 2008).

McKibben, B. (2002) 'An end to sweet illusions', [online] http://www.motherjones.com/commentary/columns/2002/01/mckibben.html, *Mother Jones Magazine*, January/February, San Francisco, CA (Accessed 24 September 2008)

Norwood, G. (2005) 'Buy an eco house and learn how to build it', *Green Building*, [online], www.newbuilder.co.uk/news/NewsFullStory.asp?offset=5&ID=616 (Accessed 24 September 2008), Carmarthenshire, Green Building Press.

Oursouthwest (n.d.) 'low carbon south west', www.oursouthwest.com/lowcarbon , Bristol, Government Office for the South West (Accessed 24 September 2008).

Pacala, S. W. and Socolow, R. H. (2004) 'Stabilization Wedges: Solving the Climate Problem for the Next 50 Years with Current Technologies', *Science*, vol. 305, no. 5686, August, pp. 968–972.

Simms, A., Johnson, V. and Smith, J. (2007) *Chinadependence: the UK Interdependence Report 2007*, London, New Economics Foundation/Milton Keynes, The Open University.

Socolow, R. H. and Pacala, S. W. (2006) 'A plan to keep carbon in check, *Scientific American*, vol. 295, no. 3, September, pp. 50–57.

Tepe, T. (2007) *August 2007 Monthly Update: International Growth in the Green Building Industry*, http://www.earthtrends.wri.org/updates/node/232 (Accessed 5 August 2008). United Nations (1992) *United Nations Framework Convention on Climate Change*, http://unfccc.int/resource/docs/convkp/conveng.pdf (Accessed 21 June 2008).

Acknowledgements

Grateful acknowledgement is made to the following sources:

Text

Delingpole, J., (2007) Polar bears in danger? Is this some kind of joke? *The Times*, November 12th 2007 © News International Syndication; McKenna, P. (2007) Climate Myths: polar bear numbers are increasing, *NewScientist.com*, 16th May 2008, © Reed Business information Limited.

Tables

Table 2.1: 'The Measure of the Twentieth Century', from *Something New Under the Sun by McNeill*, J.R. Copyright © 2000 by J.R.McNeill. Used by permission of W.W. Norton & Company, Inc.

Table 3.1: Dunster, B., Simmons, C. and Gilbert, B. (2008) *The ZEDbook. Solutions for a shrinking world*, Taylor and Francis Ltd.

Figures

Figure 1.1a: © Still Pictures; Figure 1.1b: Courtesy of Friends of the Earth, England, Wales & Northern Ireland/www.foe.co.uk; Figure 1.1c: © Greenpeace/Olivares; Figure 1.1d: © Adam Oswell/WWF-Canon; Figure 1.1e: © Photodisc; Figure 1.1f: © Edward Parker/WWF-Canon; Figure 1.1g: Courtesy of The Environment Trust; Figure 1.3a: Mountain High Maps ® Copyright © 1993 Digital Wisdom, Inc.; Figure 1.3b: Jeff Kubina/www.flickr.com; Figure 1.3c: © iStockphoto; Figure 1.3d: © National Oceanic and Atmospheric Administration/Earth System Research Laboratory; Page 24 margin: Courtesy of Scripps Institution of Oceanography; Figure 1.4: Taken from www.earthpolicy.org; Figures 1.5, 1.6 and 1.7: Courtesy of Mauna Loa Observatory/Scripps CO2 program; Figure 1.8a: Courtesy of Debra Silva; taken from http://travel.webshots.com; Figure 1.8b: © Havet/iStockphoto; Figure 1.8c: © Penny Adams/ SuperStock; Figure 1.10a: © Jean-Michel Labat/Ardea; Figure 1.10b: From http://commons.wikimedia.org/Jon Hanson; Figure 1.10c: © Dinodia Picture Agency/www.osfimages.com; Figure 1.10d: Mike Hill/osf/ Photolibrary; Figure 1.10e: © M. Watson/Ardea; Figure 1.10f: © NHPA/ Joe Blossom; Figure 1.10g: © Anup Shah/Nature Picture Library; Figure 1.10h: © Nick Gordon/Photolibrary; Figure 1.10i: © Andre Seale/ Image Quest Marine; Figures 1.12 and 1.13: Taken from *Fresh Insights*, Number 4, October 2006, International Institute for Environment and Development. Data source is Food and Agriculture Organization.

Figure 2.1: © Rex Features; Figure 2.2a: © Cambridgeshire Collection, Cambridge Central Library; Figure 2.2b: Courtesy of Joe Smith; Figure 2.3: © Tim Cuff/Alamy; Figure 2.4a: © 2008 by Andrew Alden http://geology. about.com/od/fossilcreatures/ig/Stromatolite-Gallery/Lester-Park- Stromatolites.–00.htm). Used with permission of About, Inc. which can be